The Open University

Science: a level 3 course

Mountain Building in Scotland

Prepared for the Course Team by Kevin Jones and Stephen Blake

The SXR339 Course Team

Chair
Stephen Blake

Course Manager
Jessica Bartlett (*Course Manager*)

Other members of the Course Team

Mandy Anton (*Graphic Designer*)

Gerry Bearman (*Editor*)

Steve Best (*Graphic Artist*)

Nigel Harris (*Author*)

Kevin Jones (*Consultant Author*)

Jann Matela (*Word Processing*)

Dave McGarvie (*Author*)

Ian Parkinson (*Reader*)

Val Russell (*Consultant Editor*)

Professor Rob Strachan, Oxford
  Brookes University (*Course Assessor*)

Andy Sutton (*Software Designer*)

The Course Team gratefully acknowledges the contributions of Andrew Bell and Fiona McGibbon who commented on the proofs of this book. Other contributors to SXR339 are acknowledged in specific credits.

Front cover: Gearr Aonach (left) and Aonach Dubh (right) from the Meeting of the Three Waters, Glen Coe. (*David W. Wright, Open University*)

Back cover: The view westwards from Strath Fionan, near Schiehallion, central Perthshire, to Loch Rannoch. (*Nigel Harris, Open University*)

The Open University, Walton Hall, Milton Keynes MK7 6AA.

First published 2003.

Edited, designed and typeset by The Open University.

Printed in the United Kingdom by Bath Press, Glasgow.

ISBN 0 7492 5847 0

This book forms part of an Open University course, SXR339 *Ancient Mountains: Practical Geology in Scotland*. Details of this and other Open University courses can be obtained from the Course Reservations and Sales Office, PO Box 724, The Open University, Milton Keynes MK7 6ZS, United Kingdom: tel. (00 44) 1908 653231. For availability of this or other course components, contact Open University Worldwide Ltd, Walton Hall, Milton Keynes MK7 6AA, United Kingdom: tel. (00 44) 1908 858585, fax (00 44) 1908 858787, e-mail ouwenq@open.ac.uk

Alternatively, much useful course information can be obtained from the Open University's website, http://www.open.ac.uk

1.1

1 Introduction

1.1 Setting the scene

Some of Britain's most dramatic scenery is to be found in the Scottish Highlands. The sight of mighty Ben Nevis, the desolate plateau of the Cairngorms, or the imposing landscapes of Glen Coe (pictured on the front cover) can unleash the call of the wild in all of us. Although these landforms were largely carved by glacial activity that ended some 10 000 years ago, the rocks themselves tell of a much older history. The Scottish Highlands, defined as lying north of the Highland Boundary Fault (Figure 1.1), are primarily composed of metamorphosed sedimentary and igneous rocks intruded by somewhat younger igneous bodies and cut by faults. The metamorphic rocks and igneous intrusions exposed at the surface must have formed within the Earth's crust, and this simple fact indicates that the Highlands are merely eroded stumps of a much higher range of ancient mountains. This book is an account of the origin and demise of that ancient mountain range, based on the geological evidence laid before us in rock exposures.

For well over a century, geologists have braved the rain, sun and midges to study the Highlands. Indeed, it was nineteenth-century field geologists working in northern Scotland who established several of the fundamental geological principles that are today almost taken for granted. Notable Victorian scientists such as Ben Peach, John Horne, George Barrow, Edward Bailey, Archibald Geikie, Charles Lapworth and Roderick Murchison were among those who made their names by observing and debating the significance of the rocks of the Highlands. For example, Peach and Horne, with others from the Geological Survey, mapped the rocks of north-west Scotland, recognizing an enormous low-angle fault in which ancient metamorphic rocks had been thrust tens of kilometres westwards over younger sedimentary rocks. This fault is now familiar to geologists across the world as the Moine Thrust (Figure 1.1). Working in the south-eastern Highlands around Glen Clova (Figure 1.1), George Barrow founded the concepts of metamorphic zones and index minerals, which are now universally used to map belts of regional metamorphic rocks. Another example, albeit from further south, is James Hutton's recognition, in 1788, of an unconformity at Siccar Point (Figure 1.1), where red sandstones (of Devonian age) had been deposited on upturned older (Silurian) strata. This and similar observations nearby led him to the revelation that sedimentary deposition had been interrupted by significant earth movements and erosion, requiring a truly dynamic Earth and eons of time.

Now, in the era of sophisticated geochemical, geochronological and geophysical methods, geologists are still working to make further sense of the region's dramatic geology in terms of plate tectonics and continental drift. So, the 'prodigious terrestrial displacements', recognized by Geikie to have formed the Moine Thrust, are now attributed to plate-tectonic collisions that happened almost half a billion years ago. To appreciate the classic geology of the Highlands, the basic geological field relationships remain fundamental, so this book has been written with field evidence very much to the fore.

In any story, the events that took place and the order in which they did so are critical. In the story of how the Highlands were built (and then eroded), the nature and relative timing of sedimentation, metamorphism, tectonism (folding and faulting), igneous activity and erosion are all revealed by the rocks. The evidence may come from field relationships, such as those that are pictured throughout this book, or from any one of a number of radiometric dating methods requiring high-precision laboratory instrumentation. Among the latter,

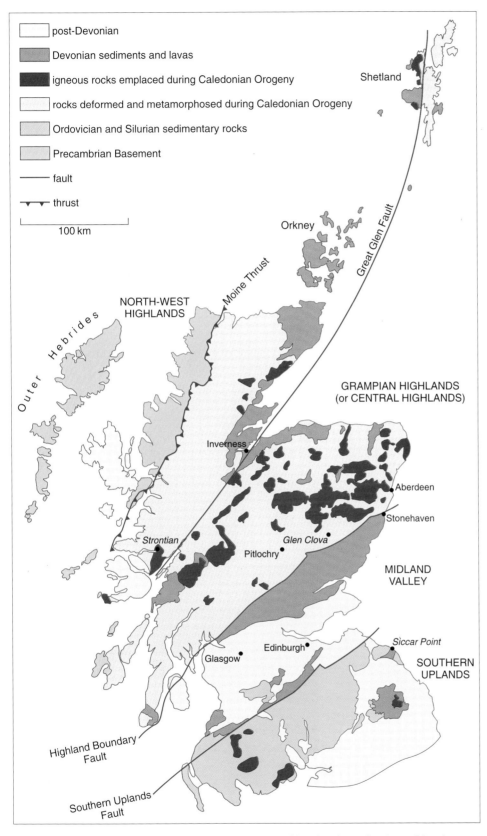

post-Devonian

Devonian sediments and lavas

igneous rocks emplaced during Caledonian Orogeny

rocks deformed and metamorphosed during Caledonian Orogeny

Ordovician and Silurian sedimentary rocks

Precambrian Basement

—— fault

▼▼▼ thrust

100 km

Shetland

Orkney

Great Glen Fault

Moine Thrust

NORTH-WEST
HIGHLANDS

Outer Hebrides

GRAMPIAN HIGHLANDS
(or CENTRAL HIGHLANDS)

Inverness

Aberdeen

Stonehaven

Strontian

Glen Clova

Pitlochry

MIDLAND
VALLEY

Siccar Point

Edinburgh

Glasgow

SOUTHERN
UPLANDS

Highland Boundary
Fault

Southern Uplands
Fault

Figure 1.1 The physical geography and geology of Scotland are dominated by the products of mountain-building events, known collectively as the Caledonian Orogeny, that took place during the Palaeozoic. Some important localities in the historical development of the geological sciences (Glen Clova, Siccar Point and Strontian) are shown in italics.

incidentally, is the rubidium–strontium method. This relies on the radiogenic isotope of strontium, an element whose name derives from the village of Strontian in Argyllshire (Figure 1.1), where the element was first discovered in the mineral strontianite.

1.2 Recognizing ancient mountains

The great modern mountain ranges of the world, such as the Himalaya, have been built over millions of years, and act as natural laboratories where Earth scientists can study the complex interplay of processes that are active during mountain building. The formation of these great mountains ranges, a process called orogeny, is inextricably linked to the forces generated by the collision of lithospheric plates at destructive plate margins. In these collision zones the crust is thickened by deformation, folding and faulting, and/or by the addition of large quantities of magma. A major consequence of tectonic crustal thickening is that rocks that were once at the surface are buried to great depths and undergo substantial modification during deformation and metamorphism (Figure 1.2).

Figure 1.2 Highly deformed and metamorphosed igneous rocks from the Borgie inlier, north coast of Scotland.

The uplift of deeply buried rocks is achieved either by erosion or by a combination of erosion and tectonic movements such as faulting, and occurs in response to the isostatic readjustment of the overthickened crust – this process is called exhumation. Eventually, over millions of years, exhumation reveals the deeper levels, or roots, of the mountain belt. It follows, therefore, that the existence of ancient mountains can be recognized by the identification of zones of highly deformed and metamorphosed rocks – these zones are called orogens or orogenic belts. The study of these ancient mountain roots provides us with a record of the processes that were active in the deep crust during collision.

1.3   Orogeny through geological time

1.3.1   Geological time: a brief note

Geological time can be divided into Eons, Eras and Periods, with further subdivisions into Epochs and Ages (Figure 1.3). The order of rock units determined from the principles of superposition and faunal succession produces the lithostratigraphic column, which is based simply on the relative ages of rocks, e.g. Llandovery is younger than Ashgill but older than Wenlock. A second aspect of the stratigraphic column relates to the chronostratigraphic dating of rock units, which allows geologists to apply absolute ages to rock successions, e.g. the Llandovery ranges from 443–428 Ma.

Eon	Era	Period	Epoch	Age	Ma
PHANEROZOIC	PALAEOZOIC	Permian	Late	Zechstein	248
					256
			Early	Rotliegendes	290
		Carboniferous	Silesian	Stephanian	305
				Westphalian	315
				Namurian	327
			Dinantian	Viséan	342
				Tournaisian	362
		Devonian	Late	Famennian	377
				Frasnian	383
			Mid	Givetian	388
				Eifelian	394
			Early	Emsian	410
				Pragian	414
				Lochkovian	418
		Silurian	Late	Pridoli	419
				Ludlow	423
			Early	Wenlock	428
				Llandovery	443
		Ordovician	Late	Ashgill	449
				Caradoc	462
			Mid	Llanvirn	470
			Early	Arenig	485
				Tremadoc	495
		Cambrian	Late		505
			Mid		518
			Early		545
CRYPTOZOIC or PRECAMBRIAN	PROTEROZOIC	Neoproterozoic			1000
		Mesoproterozoic			1600
		Palaeoproterozoic			2500
	ARCHAEAN	Late Archaean			3000
		Middle Archaean			3500
		Early Archaean			4000
	HADEAN				4560

Figure 1.3   Part of the geological time-scale, showing chronostratigraphic subdivisions. Note that formally defined divisions start with an upper case letter (e.g. Mid-Ordovician), whereas informally defined divisions (e.g. mid-Silurian) start with a lower case letter. Accordingly, Early Devonian has a specific meaning or definition, whereas early Devonian is less specific.

1.3.2 Disentangling the continents

The dating of crystalline rocks using radiogenic isotopes has become a prerequisite to understanding and unravelling regions of complexly deformed and metamorphosed rocks. For several decades, radiogenic isotope systems have been used to date events such as the crystallization of metamorphic and igneous rocks. With the advent of new analytical methods it is now possible to date the crystallization of individual minerals (or even parts of minerals) such as zircon or garnet, to a precision of one or two million years, even in the oldest Precambrian rocks. Our knowledge of continental geology owes much to these methods. For instance, we now know that the succession of collisions or orogenies that have built the present-day continents occurred over long expanses of geological time.

Orogenic belts can be made up of several displaced crustal fragments, called terranes, which may have travelled thousands of kilometres across the Earth's surface before colliding with and accreting to an existing continental margin. These terranes can be oceanic crust, island arcs, or pieces of continental crust carried by subducting plates and plastered to continental margins when the plates collided. The collision 'scar' or suture zone may preserve relicts of the oceanic crust that once separated the crustal fragments – these relicts are called ophiolites.

The rocks that preserve a record of the oldest or most ancient orogenic episodes usually form the core or interior parts of continents – these are known as shield areas or cratons. These regions are often surrounded by a series of younger, more recently active mountain belts, which form long, relatively narrow topographic features such as the Alpine–Himalayan chain of southern Europe and Asia. As successively younger orogenic belts develop around the margins of the continents, the older orogenic belts that are exposed to these events become incorporated within the younger orogenies, and as a result are progressively reworked. During this process of reworking, the record of the earlier periods of orogeny becomes progressively overprinted by younger events, and so an incomplete record of orogeny is preserved.

Several factors may lead to problems in reconstructing the history of ancient orogens. Remnants of older orogens are often obscured and lie beneath younger sedimentary rocks. The older rocks may have complex histories resulting from multiple episodes of deformation, metamorphism and magmatism, which in many cases cannot be resolved even by conventional isotopic methods. The diachronous nature of the successive collisions and accretion of crustal fragments to continental margins during orogeny causes problems of correlation along the belt. In addition, details of early collisions are often obscured by later accretion events. For example, plate boundary histories are difficult to unravel if large-scale strike–slip fault systems have been active at different times.

1.4 The collage of ancient orogenic belts in the North Atlantic region

The geology of the Scottish Highlands is dominated by the effects of the last great mountain building event to have affected the region – the Caledonian Orogeny. However, the Highlands represents only a small fragment of an orogenic belt that was once of much greater extent. Fragments of this early Palaeozoic orogenic belt are scattered across the North Atlantic region as a result

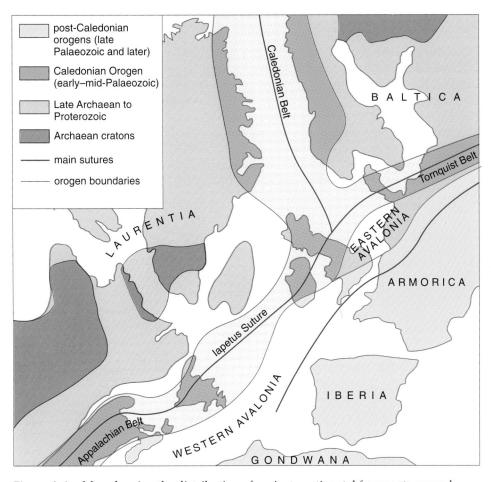

Figure 1.4 Map showing the distribution of ancient continental fragments around Britain and Ireland prior to the opening of the present-day Atlantic Ocean. The age assigned to different continental fragments is that of the most dominant period of orogeny. The younger orogenic belts are built on reworked older orogenic belts. Light shades indicate areas where the geological reconstruction is inferred.

of the opening of the present-day Atlantic Ocean. A reconstruction of the position of the continents prior to this opening clearly demonstrates the extent of the Caledonian Orogenic Belt (Figure 1.4).

Examination of Figure 1.4 reveals that the Caledonian Orogenic Belt (the Caledonides) has three distinct arms: a northern Caledonian Belt, a western Appalachian Belt and an eastern Tornquist Belt. These belts or branches separate parts of three major palaeocontinents that preserve records of much older orogenic episodes, e.g. the palaeocontinent of Laurentia is composed of rock units that were subjected to major periods of orogeny in both the Archaean and the Proterozoic. The three palaeocontinents of Laurentia (North America and Greenland), Baltica (Scandinavia and the Baltic) and Avalonia (southern Ireland and Britain) drifted together in the early Palaeozoic, colliding to form the Caledonian Orogenic Belt. Britain and Ireland hold a special position in this orogenic system as they straddle the Caledonian Orogen, adjacent to the three palaeocontinents.

1.5   What caused the Caledonian Orogeny?

The tectonics that led to the construction of the Caledonian Orogenic Belt were associated with the closure of a major ocean called Iapetus. The Caledonian Orogeny was not a simple continent–continent collision, it encompassed a series of more localized arc–arc, arc–continent and continent–continent collisions. The sequence of events that led to the collision of Laurentia, Baltica and Avalonia, and to the formation of the Caledonian Orogenic Belt, can be traced as far back in time as *c.* 600 Ma, to the break-up of a major palaeocontinental landmass referred to as the Vendian Supercontinent, named after the Vendian Period (*c.* 680–545 Ma). This sequence of events is illustrated on Figure 1.5 and can be summarized as follows:

- The initial break-up of the Vendian Supercontinent began *c.* 600–580 Ma ago with Baltica rifting from eastern Laurentia along the Greenland margin, and Gondwana rifting from North America, thus forming the Iapetus Ocean (Figures 1.5a,b).

- The initial stages of ocean destruction began in Cambrian to Early Ordovician times with the formation of subduction zones and the localized collision of volcanic arcs along the margins of the continents that surrounded Iapetus (Figures 1.5c,d). The phase of arc–continent collisions along the southern margin of Laurentia is referred to as the Grampian orogenic phase, evidence for which can be seen in the rocks of Scotland and Ireland.

- Also at this time the continent of Gondwana began to break up, and continental fragments, including Avalonia, which incorporated southern Britain, rifted and migrated northwards, narrowing the intervening Iapetus Ocean and opening another, the Rheic Ocean, in its wake (Figure 1.5d).

- The initial collision of Avalonian fragments with the Laurentian margin (Figure 1.5e) occurred between *c.* 470 Ma and *c.* 440 Ma. The final closure of Iapetus was in the Silurian (*c.* 425 Ma), with Baltica and parts of Avalonia converging obliquely with the Laurentian margin (Figure 1.5f), resulting in the Scandian orogenic phase. At this time, significant strike–slip displacements associated with oblique collision disrupted the Laurentian margin and the Iapetus Suture Zone.

1.6   The tectonic map of Britain and Ireland

The Caledonian Orogeny was primarily responsible for the consolidation of the British Isles into its present pattern of fault-bounded crustal blocks. These crustal blocks are terranes that represent displaced fragments of continents, volcanic arcs or ocean basins accreted to the continental margins by combinations of subduction, collision and strike–slip displacement. Each of these terranes has its own individual and distinct history. The terranes and major terrane-bounding faults of Britain and Ireland are illustrated in Figure 1.6.

These terranes are subdivided into three main groups:

- *Laurentian Terranes*: those to the north of the Highland Boundary Fault – Fair Head–Clew Bay Line, which have evolved as part of Laurentia (Hebridean, Northern Highlands and Central Highlands Terranes).

- *Gondwanan Terranes*: those to the south of the Solway Line, which are thought to have evolved as part of Gondwana (Leinster–Lakesman, Monian, Welsh Basin and Midland Platform Terranes).

- *Intermediate Accreted Terranes*: an intervening zone consisting of slivers of continental margin, island arc and oceanic rocks (Midland Valley and Southern Uplands Terranes) that form a complex suture zone separating Laurentia and the Gondwanan Terranes.

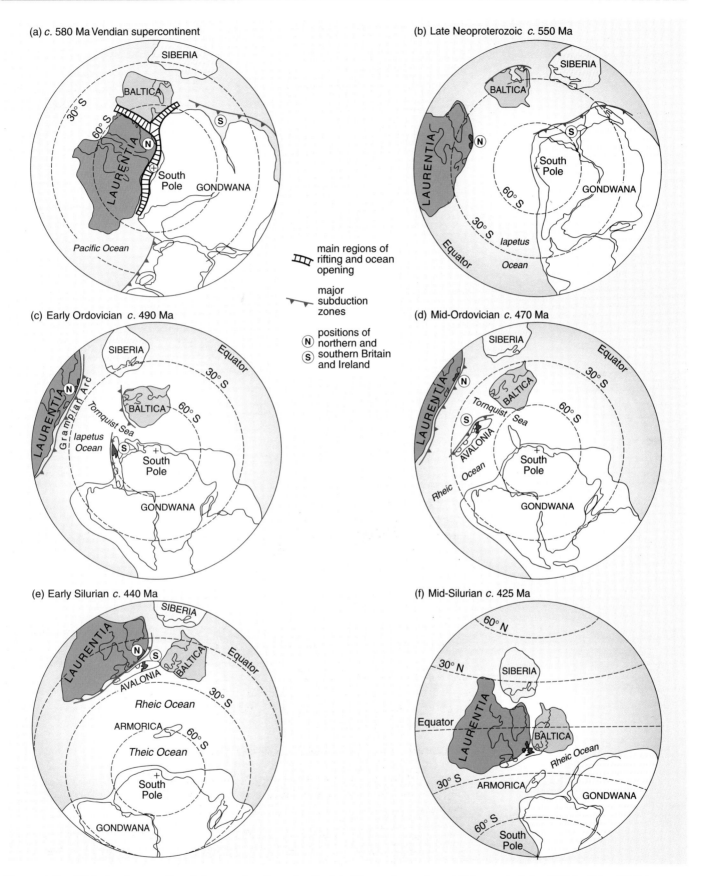

Figure 1.5 Global palaeocontinental reconstructions for the late Neoproterozoic and Palaeozoic: (a) *c.* 580 Ma; (b) *c.* 550 Ma; (c) *c.* 490 Ma; (d) *c.* 470 Ma; (e) *c.* 440 Ma; (f) *c.* 425 Ma.

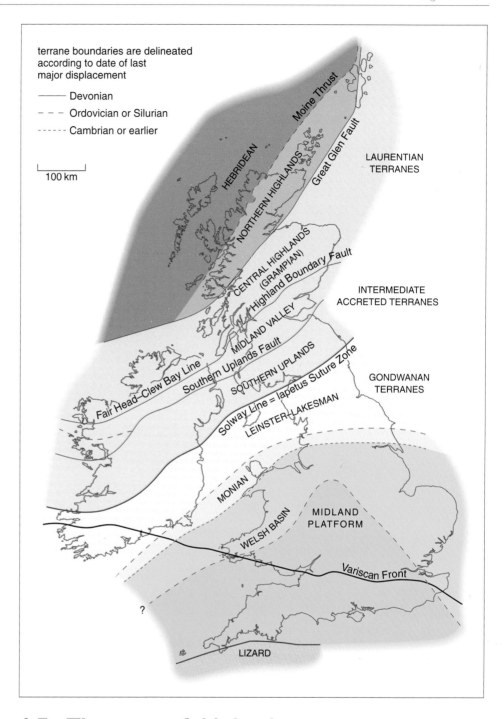

terrane boundaries are delineated
according to date of last
major displacement

—— Devonian

– – – Ordovician or Silurian

------ Cambrian or earlier

100 km

Figure 1.6 Simplified Palaeozoic
terrane map of Britain and Ireland.

1.7 The scope of this book

The Scottish Highlands contains some of the most extensively studied areas of
geology in the world. Given the fact that the region is of relatively small size, it is
perhaps surprising that the rocks of the Scottish Highlands preserve a record of at
least six periods of mountain building, which occurred over considerable
geological time. In this book we will examine the nature of the evidence and the
methods employed by geologists to unravel the complex history of this particular
region. As mentioned in Section 1.4, the Caledonian Orogeny was the last major
mountain-building event to have left an imprint on this region. In Sections 2 and 3
we will see glimpses of several older orogenic episodes from the Archaean and
Proterozoic Eras. These serve to outline the basic concepts and principles of
orogenesis, from which a more detailed study of the Caledonian Orogeny can be
undertaken. Sections 4 to 9 focus on unravelling what happened during and after
the Caledonian Orogeny.

2 Britain's oldest rocks: remnants of Archaean crust

2.1 Introduction

Owing to the complex nature of extremely old deformed rocks, the standard methods that are used to establish a stratigraphic evolution cannot be applied. Instead, geologists are reliant upon establishing the sequence of deformation, metamorphism and intrusion of igneous rocks, and the isotopic dating of these events. The application of ever more sophisticated isotopic-dating techniques is changing our perception of the evolution of these extremely old rocks. The interpretation of data from such rocks is often complex and subtle, and is invariably of a controversial nature. As a consequence, this Section only provides a broad overview of the current state of knowledge of the events and processes recorded in Britain's most ancient rocks.

2.2 The Lewisian Complex

The oldest rocks of the British Isles are Mid- to Late Archaean in age and are exposed on the mainland of north-west Scotland, and on the Inner and Outer Hebrides (Figure 2.1). These rocks are mainly deformed and metamorphosed igneous rocks – orthogneisses (Figure 2.2) – and are collectively termed the Lewisian Complex, after the Isle of Lewis in the Outer Hebrides.

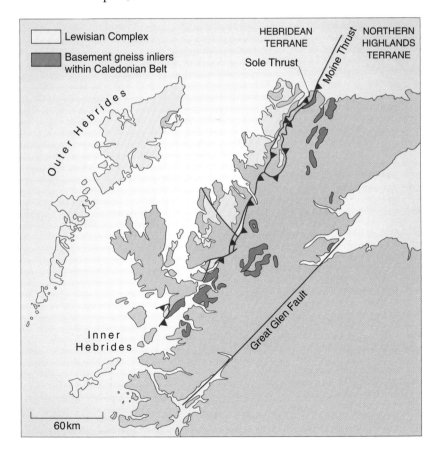

Figure 2.1 Location of Archaean rocks of the Lewisian Complex and Archaean inliers in north-west Scotland.

Figure 2.2 Typical Lewisian gneisses showing intense deformation, Pollachar, South Uist, Outer Hebrides.

Recent studies have established that the Lewisian Complex exposed on the Scottish mainland comprises a series of crustal blocks (terranes) that evolved separately before they were welded together by collision during the Palaeoproterozoic. At least four terranes are now recognized: from north to south they are the Rhiconich, Assynt, Gruinard and Southern Region Terranes (Figure 2.3).

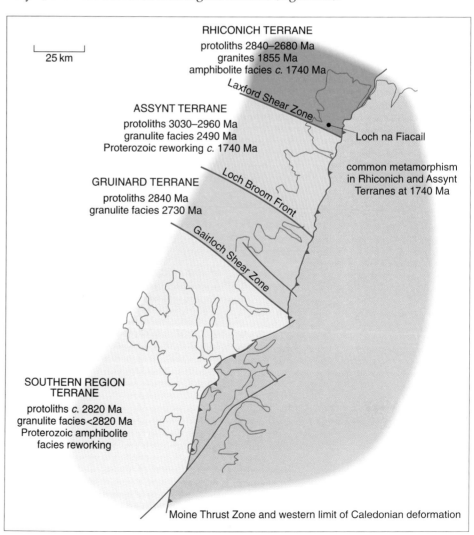

Figure 2.3 Sketch map of the Lewisian Complex exposed on the Scottish mainland. The ages of the protoliths or parent rocks and the main metamorphic events used to constrain the boundaries between the terranes are shown.

Each of the terranes has its own individual history, yet collectively they record a sequence of geological events spanning some 1300 million years. The individual terranes are separated by steeply dipping shear zones: the Laxford Shear Zone, Loch Broom Front and Gairloch Shear Zone. The magnitude of displacement across these shear zones, and hence the original relationships between different terranes, is uncertain and the subject of much debate.

2.2.1　The nature, age and origin of the gneiss protoliths

The parent rocks, or protoliths, of the gneisses exposed in the Assynt Terrane have been identified using field evidence and geochemical evidence. In areas of low tectonic strain, intrusive cross-cutting relationships are still preserved (Figure 2.4), pointing to an igneous origin for these Assynt gneisses. Their chemical compositions reflect their origin as mafic and acidic plutonic rocks: gabbros, granodiorites, tonalites and trondhjemites. These rocks are often referred to as basement complexes.

Figure 2.4　Primary intrusive relationships from the Lewisian Complex, Gruinard Bay. The early mafic intrusives are invaded by veins of later granodiorite.

Radiometric dating (using U and Pb isotopes) of zircon crystals from the protoliths of the gneisses in the various terranes have yielded a variety of Late Archaean ages (*c.* 3030–2680 Ma, see Figure 2.3) that are interpreted as recording the time of magmatic crystallization. Interestingly, the core of one zircon crystal from a suite of gneisses from Loch na Fiacail, in the Rhiconich Terrane (for sample location see Figure 2.3), has given an age of *c.* 3550 Ma, and represents the oldest dated mineral from this region (Figure 2.5). The origin of this older core is enigmatic.

Figure 2.5 Is this the oldest mineral in Britain? Photomicrograph (a) and cathodoluminescence image (b) of a single zircon crystal from Loch na Fiacail. The core of this crystal has given an age of *c.* 3550 Ma, whereas the rim gives a much younger age of *c.* 2840 Ma and is interpreted as dating the time of magmatic crystallization. Three kidney-shaped pits in the core of the crystal and one on the rim, visible in (b), were formed when the sample was bombarded by a beam of ions during analysis. The scale bar in (b) represents 100 µm.

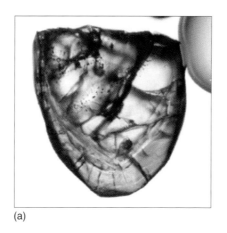
(a)

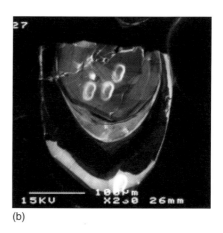
(b)

The chemical compositions of the gneisses indicate that they are related to magmas generated at subduction zones, whereas mafic and ultramafic rocks that are found in association with minor metasedimentary and metavolcanic rocks are broadly comparable with modern tholeiitic basalts. The rocks are therefore thought to have originated in oceanic island-arc environments.

2.2.2 Deformation and high-grade metamorphism

The Archaean protoliths of the Assynt, Gruinard and Southern Region Terranes suffered intense deformation and metamorphism (often referred to as crustal reworking) that led to the formation of gneisses and crystallization of high-grade granulite-facies metamorphic assemblages (Box 2.1). These gneisses are collectively termed the Scourian gneisses. Isotope geochronology has indicated that deformation and granulite-facies metamorphism occurred at different times within the individual terranes during the Late Archaean to earliest Proterozoic, *c.* >2820–2490 Ma (Figure 2.3).

The most complete record of granulite-facies events is preserved, albeit locally, in areas which have escaped subsequent reworking by later events. In the Assynt Terrane, intense deformation led to the formation of a sub-horizontal gneissic foliation, strong lineation and isoclinal folding. Here conditions of metamorphism have been estimated at 1000 °C and 1100 MPa, and isotopic dating of metamorphic zircons, thought to have grown during granulite-facies metamorphism, has given ages of *c.* 2490–2480 Ma. The achievement of such high temperatures and pressures probably resulted from tectonic thickening during a collisional orogenic event. The gneisses are also depleted in U, Th, Rb and Pb, a characteristic feature of many terranes metamorphosed under granulite facies. This chemical signature indicates that the rocks are the residues left behind after partial melting and melt extraction accompanying granulite-facies metamorphism. Subsequently, the granulites experienced amphibolite-facies metamorphism, where conditions fell to 500–625 °C and 300–600 MPa, indicating considerable cooling and uplift/erosion of the crust.

In contrast, the Rhiconich Terrane preserves no evidence of having been reworked under granulite-facies conditions during the Late Archaean to early Palaeoproterozoic. For example, granulite-facies mineral assemblages and geochemical evidence of melting processes are lacking. The rocks of this terrane have clearly not experienced a granulite-facies event and must therefore have evolved in a different tectonic setting or crustal level.

Box 2.1 Metamorphic facies

Metamorphic facies is a term used to embrace all possible metamorphic minerals in rocks metamorphosed under the same conditions of pressure and temperature. Individual facies correspond to the range of pressure (P) and temperature (T) conditions under which a particular set of minerals is stable. The position of the facies on a P–T diagram represents the experimentally-determined stability fields of mineral assemblages in rocks of a range of bulk compositions (Figure 2.6). Metamorphic facies therefore provide a general range of P–T conditions over which the rocks have crystallized.

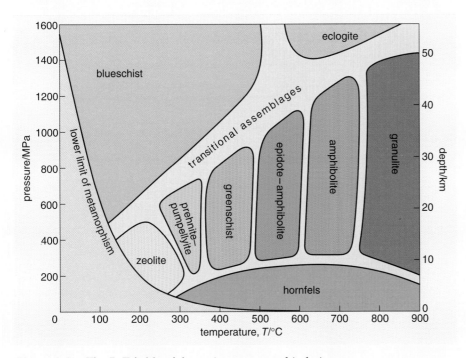

Figure 2.6   The P–T fields of the major metamorphic facies.

2.3   Basement inliers in the Moine Supergroup

A series of orthogneisses and associated minor metasediments occur as inliers within rocks of the Moine Supergroup, to the east of the Moine Thrust (Figure 2.1). These inliers are thought to represent examples of the high-grade basement upon which the Neoproterozoic Moine Supergroup was deposited (Section 3.6.2). An Archaean protolith age of c. 2800 Ma has been obtained on one of the basement inliers from the north coast of Scotland. The conventional view, based simply on the similar appearance in the field of these gneisses, has been that these rocks belong to, and once formed part of, the Lewisian Complex, yet there is no sound geological reason to assume this is the case. These rocks may in fact belong to one of several different Archaean basement terrane(s) which are entirely unrelated to the Lewisian Complex, and further research is needed to resolve this issue.

2.4   Summary of Section 2

- Isotopic and geochemical evidence indicates that the Archaean continental crust grew by the separation of magma from the mantle, probably as a result of subduction processes, over a time span of about 350 million years.

- The Lewisian Complex is composed of a series of disparate terranes each having an individual history. The earliest orogenic events, high-grade metamorphism and intense deformation, occurred at different times within each terrane. Mineral assemblages and pressure and temperature estimates indicate that metamorphism resulted from considerable crustal thickening.

- Several basement inliers, Archaean in age, of uncertain affinity are exposed to the east of the Moine Thrust.

3 Orogenies in the Proterozoic

3.1 Introduction

Orogenies in the Proterozoic are thought to have resulted from the collision of large continental blocks and the closure of intervening oceans. These orogenic episodes are often recognized by the presence of three geological features: 1) calc-alkaline igneous rocks formed during subduction; 2) discrete suture zones containing ophiolites; and 3) remnants of high-pressure regional metamorphism that indicate periods of crustal thickening. The amalgamation of continental blocks or fragments led to the formation of large individual continental masses known as supercontinents. The periodic break-up of supercontinents led to the formation of extensive passive margins where thick sedimentary sequences accumulated. Subsequent collisions of continental fragments formed extensive linear mountain belts.

Although Britain and Ireland only represent a small area of crust, the various basement complexes and sedimentary sequences of Proterozoic age provide a record of plate reorganizations that occurred during the time period from c. 2500 Ma to c. 750 Ma. The major rock units and geological events that date from this time are summarized in Figure 3.1 and discussed in this Section,

Figure 3.1   A summary of the geographical and time relationships of Late Archaean to Late Proterozoic rocks and events discussed in Sections 2, 3 and 4 of this book.

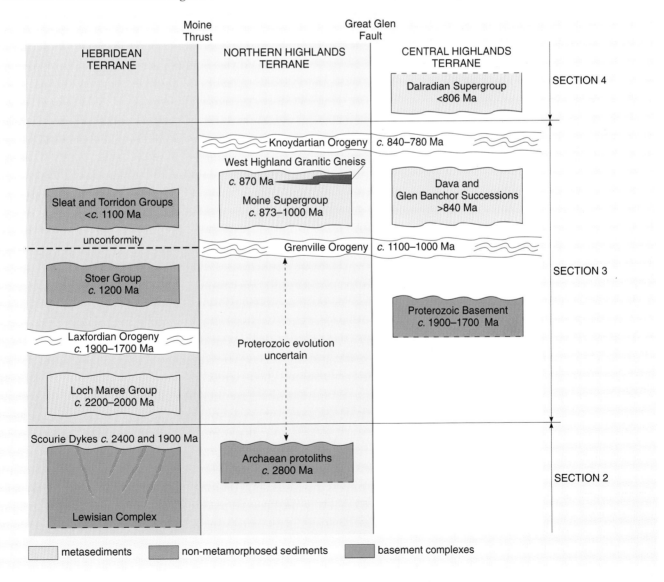

from which the following points will emerge:

- Proterozoic rocks outcrop in three fault-bounded terranes.

- The boundaries between the various rock units in each terrane are regionally important unconformities; in other words, they are gaps in the geological record that identify periods of crustal shortening, uplift and erosion.

- Metamorphism and magmatism were associated with the orogenic episodes.

- Between these orogenic episodes there were major periods of sediment accumulation, often associated with crustal extension.

- Basement orthogneiss complexes identify major periods of primary crustal growth, some evidence for which was discussed in Section 2.

3.2   Palaeoproterozoic rifting, sedimentation and magmatism

We have already seen that continental growth in the Archaean was achieved by magma addition and that these rocks were involved in collision-related events that continued into the early Palaeoproterozoic. In the Lewisian Complex, and in particular in the Assynt Terrane, a terrane that largely escaped Proterozoic deformation (see Section 3.3.1), the structures and fabrics formed during granulite-facies metamorphism and the subsequent amphibolite-facies metamorphism are cross-cut by mafic dyke swarms, collectively known as the Scourie dykes (Figure 3.2). In areas of low strain, these dykes contain primary igneous textures and mineralogies, and often retain chilled margins against the surrounding gneisses.

Figure 3.2   A Scourie dyke (left of the contact marked in white) intruding Lewision gneiss containing an earlier, near-horizontal foliation, Balgey, Loch Torridon, north-west Scotland. Note that the margin of the dyke is slightly foliated as a result of later deformation.

The dykes were emplaced into crust for which ambient temperature and pressure conditions were 450–550 °C and 400–500 MPa. Isotopic dating of these dykes has identified two discrete swarms that were emplaced at *c.* 2420 Ma and *c.* 1990 Ma. The occurrence of mafic dyke swarms is usually linked to wholesale crustal thinning or rifting and signifies periods of lithospheric extension. The interpretation of the dyke swarms in the Lewisian Complex is no exception. Mafic dyke swarms have also been identified within the other terranes of the Lewisian Complex and all are thought to be linked to phases of crustal extension and rifting.

The record of sedimentation in the Palaeoproterozoic is limited to the Loch Maree Group, which occurs within the Gruinard Terrane of the Lewisian Complex (Figure 3.3). The Loch Maree Group comprises two components: one is oceanic and includes shallow marine plateau basalts and abyssal sediments, the other is continental and consists of greywackes and deltaic sediments. Dating of detrital minerals from the continental sediments indicates a provenance (see Box 3.1) from both Archaean and Palaeoproterozoic sources and indicates a maximum age of deposition for the Loch Maree Group of *c.* 2200–2000 Ma.

- What is the style of tectonism implied by the timing of dyke emplacement and sedimentation?

- The widespread occurrence of mafic dyke swarms at *c.* 2420 Ma and *c.* 1990 Ma that are broadly correlated with sedimentation at *c.* 2200–2000 Ma is considered to reflect the break-up by rifting of the Archaean to Early Proterozoic crust into smaller continental fragments separated by oceanic tracts. The occurrence of rocks of oceanic affinity within the Loch Maree Group indicates that rifting eventually led to rupture of the crust and formation of oceanic lithosphere.

Box 3.1 Provenance studies

Provenance studies involve the petrographical, chemical and isotopic analysis of the rock and mineral fragments within sediments to provide important information on the sediment source regions, which were usually mountain belts that were undergoing erosion at the time of sedimentation. These types of data, along with palaeocurrent information, can be used to identify the existence of ancient mountain belts. Furthermore, in the absence of palaeontological data, the timing of sedimentation in (meta)sedimentary rocks can normally be bracketed by dating pre- and post-depositional orogenic events, e.g. magmatism, deformation and metamorphism, or by the isotopic dating of syn-sedimentary volcanic deposits. In recent years advances in the chemical fingerprinting and isotopic dating of mineral grains has improved our understanding of the provenance of older (meta)sediments and the timing of their deposition.

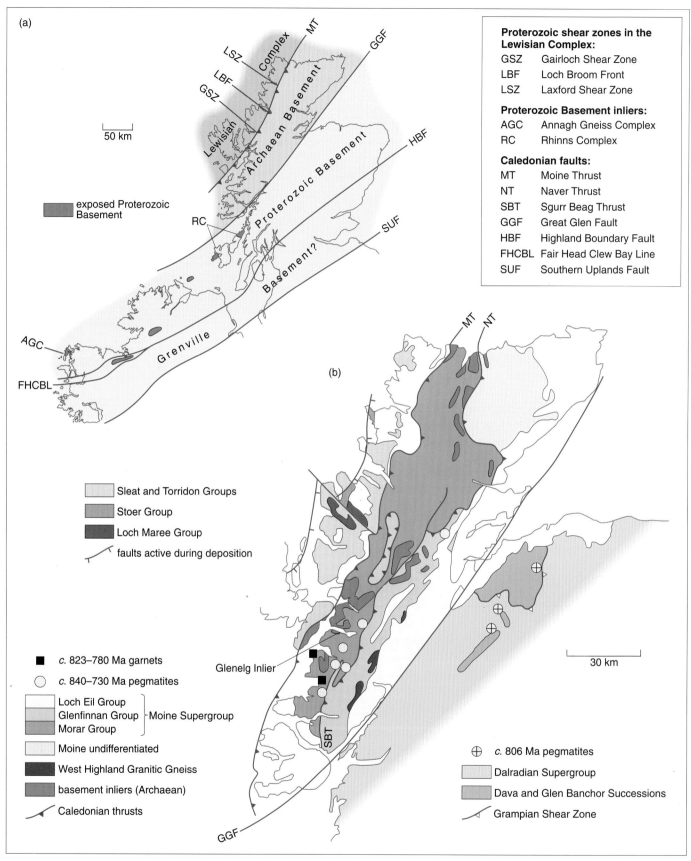

Figure 3.3 (a) Tectonic subdivision of the Caledonides. Areas thought to be underlain by various basement types and the location of Proterozoic shear zones in the Lewisian Complex are indicated. (b) Location of Proterozoic rocks.

3.3   The Palaeoproterozoic Laxfordian Orogeny

The sequence of tectonic events spanning *c.* 2000–1600 Ma provides a record of the convergence of continental blocks and the subsequent development of an active plate margin. The Palaeoproterozoic *c.* 1900–1750 Ma Laxfordian orogenic event records the closure of minor oceanic basins and the progressive accretion of terranes that eventually amalgamated to form a larger continental mass. The emplacement of mantle-derived magmas at *c.* 1900–1780 Ma suggests the formation of a subduction zone along the margin of this continental mass. Evidence for these events is preserved in the Lewisian Complex of north-west Scotland, the Rhinns Complex of the Inner Hebrides, and the Annagh Gneiss Complex of north-west Ireland (Figure 3.3a).

3.3.1   Assembly of the Lewisian Complex

Widespread deformation and metamorphism of the Lewisian Complex between *c.* 2000–1750 Ma resulted from the progressive amalgamation of the Rhiconich, Assynt, Gruinard and Southern Region Terranes. In the Gruinard Terrane, deformation, metamorphism and magmatism in the Loch Maree Group record an early phase of the Laxfordian deformation and are related to the accretion of oceanic and volcanic arc components to the upper plate of a subduction zone formed between two converging continental blocks (Figure 3.4).

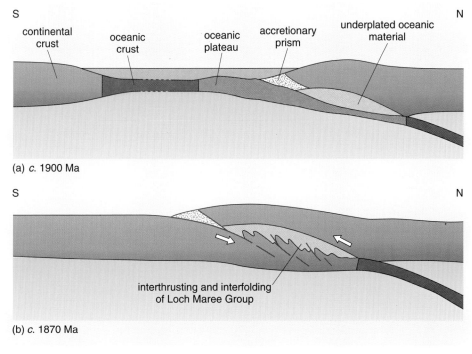

Figure 3.4   Cartoon illustrating the possible structural development of the Loch Maree Group. (a) Accretionary prism and underplated oceanic material represent the protoliths of the Loch Maree Group. (b) Interthrusting and interfolding of the Loch Maree Group as a result of subduction and plate collision.

Melting of the subducted oceanic crust led to granodioritic magmas that were emplaced into the complex at *c.* 1900 Ma. Metamorphic conditions reached amphibolite facies (*c.* 530–630 °C) and suggest that the crust was being thickened at this time. A later sequence of deformation events (*c.* 1700 Ma) led to the formation of upright folds and shear zones that probably record continued or renewed convergence.

Elsewhere in the Lewisian Complex, Laxfordian deformation and metamorphism are associated with regional-scale folding and formation of major ductile shear zones (Figure 3.5). Several of these shear zones are interpreted as terrane-bounding structures: the Laxford Shear Zone, the Loch Broom Front and the Gairloch Shear Zone (Figure 2.3). Figure 3.6 is a simplified cross-section illustrating the complex geological relationships across the Laxford Shear Zone, a structure that marks the boundary between the Rhiconich and Assynt Terranes.

Figure 3.5   Laxfordian deformation of Archaean gneisses of the Rhiconich Terrane at Rispond Beach, north coast of Scotland. The steep, near-vertical fabric is a shear zone formed during intense Laxfordian deformation. The dark inclusions in the paler gneisses are interpreted as boudins of intensely deformed mafic dykes. Width of view *c.* 25 m.

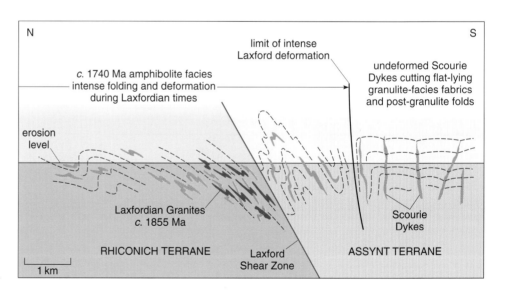

Figure 3.6   Simplified cross-section showing Laxfordian deformation across the Rhiconich–Assynt Terrane boundary and the Laxford Shear Zone.

Only the Assynt Terrane escaped this major period of crustal reworking, and so near pristine granulite-facies rocks and structures are still preserved (Figure 3.6). Here deformation is weak and non-pervasive and is concentrated along previously formed steeply-dipping shear zones and the margins of the Scourie dykes. In these shear zones, the early granulite-facies fabrics are reoriented and the magmatic fabrics of the dykes are strongly foliated and brought into parallelism with the dyke margins; a transformation that can be observed by comparing Figures 3.2 and 3.7.

Figure 3.7   Laxfordian deformation showing parallel foliation (yellow lines) in a Scourie dyke and its surrounding gneisses, Loch Tritlean, north-west Scotland.

Along the northern edge of the Laxford Shear Zone, early Laxfordian granitic sheets (*c.* 1855 Ma) are strongly deformed under amphibolite-facies conditions (Figure 3.8). These granites are not observed in the Assynt Terrane (Figure. 3.6).

Figure 3.8   Laxfordian deformation at Loch na Fiacail (for location see Figure 2.3). On the section the Archaean gneisses (gn) are cut by mafic dykes (md) and both are cross-cut by granitic pegmatites (gp). The oldest dated mineral in Britain (Figure 2.5) came from a sample of the gneiss from this locality. The regularly spaced, near vertical lines were formed during construction of the road cutting.

Radiometric dating of amphibolite-facies metamorphism in the Rhiconich and Assynt Terranes gives ages of *c.* 1740 Ma.

⬤ What are the tectonic implications of the similar ages recorded from these two terranes?

⬤ Whereas the absence of Laxfordian granites in the Assynt Terrane indicates that the two terranes must have been juxtaposed after *c.* 1855 Ma (the intrusion age of the granitic sheets), the common metamorphic ages of *c.* 1740 Ma suggest that the two terranes probably amalgamated at *c.* 1740 Ma or somewhat earlier.

⬤ The proposed tectonic boundary between the Assynt and Gruinard Terranes, the Loch Broom Front, is located on Figure 2.3. Given the data presented in Figure 2.3, determine a maximum age for terrrane accretion along this boundary.

⬤ The Assynt and Gruinard Terranes were accreted along the Loch Broom Front after *c.* 2490 Ma. We know this because *c.* 2490 Ma is the age of the youngest granulite-facies event to have affected the Assynt Terrane but not the Gruinard Terrane.

3.3.2 Formation of Proterozoic crust

Basement rocks of Palaeoproterozoic age are exposed in small fault-bounded inliers – the Annagh Gneiss Complex of north-west Ireland and a series of inliers collectively termed the Rhinns Complex of the Inner Hebrides (Figure 3.3a). The Rhinns Complex comprises weakly deformed and metamorphosed alkaline igneous rocks, syenites and gabbros, which have geochemical signatures consistent with formation in a subduction-related magmatic arc. The syenites have been dated at *c.* 1782 Ma and *c.* 1779 Ma. Amphiboles from the Rhinns Complex have given ages of *c.* 1710 Ma, and these younger ages are interpreted as recording cooling of the complexes following metamorphism. Isotopic studies indicate that the rocks of the Rhinns Complex formed as newly differentiated (juvenile) mantle-derived materials. The Annagh Gneiss Complex of north-west Ireland consists of a series of orthogneisses cut by granites and metabasic dykes (Figure 3.9). The igneous protoliths of some of the rocks have yielded radiometric ages of *c.* 1900 Ma.

The Rhinns and Annagh Gneiss Complexes, although small in area, provide an important record of Palaeoproterozic events. Several indirect lines of evidence indicate that this Palaeoproterozoic basement has a much greater extent (Figure 3.3a). Its existence at depth has been inferred from the isotopic signatures of Caledonian granites and Tertiary dykes that have incorporated older, so-called inherited, components from deeper crustal levels. These inherited basement components have given an age range of *c.* 1960–1850 Ma. Furthermore, regional gravity and magnetic data indicate that low-density, highly magnetic basement, which is unlike the Lewisian Complex, lies beneath both the Midland Valley and much of the Central Highlands Terrane. Provenance studies of locally-derived granitic boulders in younger sediments (Neoproterozoic glacial tillites within the Dalradian Supergroup) show them to be petrographically and chemically similar to components of the Rhinns Complex. These data suggest that rocks found in the Rhinns Complex were once much more widespread.

Figure 3.9 Palaeoproterozoic orthogneisses of the Annagh Gneiss Complex cross-cut by later granite sheets (of Grenville age, *c.* 1100–1000 Ma).

3.4 Synthesis: the broader view of Palaeoproterozoic events

Reconstructing the palaeocontinental blocks in the North Atlantic region indicates that the Lewisian Complex formed part of a continuous Palaeoproterozoic orogenic belt linking the Canadian Shield (Labrador Belt) with Greenland (Nagssugtoqidian and Ammassalik Belts) and Scandinavia (Lapland–Kola Belt) (Figure 3.10).

Figure 3.10 Reconstruction of the Palaeoproterozoic orogenic belts and Archaean cratons of the North Atlantic region.

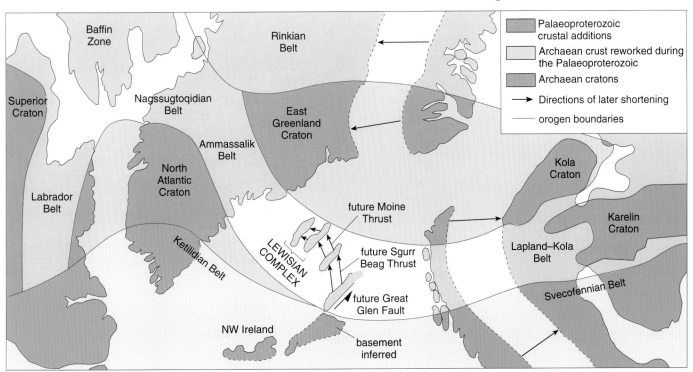

This belt comprises mainly Archaean rocks that were deformed and metamorphosed at *c.* 1900–1800 Ma. Crustal thickening and metamorphism are thought to have resulted from the collision of the various continental blocks, which followed oceanic closure by subduction. The convergence of continental blocks between *c.* 1900 Ma and *c.* 1600 Ma resulted in the formation of a broadly continuous continent that included Laurentia and Baltica. A major subduction zone developed along the southern margin of this supercontinent and led to the formation of juvenile Palaeoproterozoic materials between *c.* 1900 and *c.* 1600 Ma. This event is correlated with the Ketilidian Belt of Greenland and the Svecofennian Belt of Scandinavia (Figure 3.10).

3.5   Mesoproterozoic events

In the British Isles there is only rather isolated evidence for Mesoproterozoic events. The supercontinent that was assembled in the Palaeoproterozoic by the amalgamation of Archaean terranes is thought to have existed until *c.* 1400–1300 Ma. A limited record of Mesoproterozoic sedimentation provides evidence of extension and rifting, whereas basement inliers of metamorphic rocks give glimpses of the late Mesoproterozoic Grenville Orogeny *c.* 1100–1000 Ma.

3.5.1   Mesoproterozoic rifting: deposition of the Stoer Group

The Stoer Group outcrops in north-west Scotland (Figure 3.3b) and is a sequence of continental sedimentary rocks comprising aeolian, fluvial and deltaic deposits. They rest unconformably on the Lewisian Complex and fill an eroded Lewisian landscape (Figure 3.11).

Figure 3.11   Basal unconformity (white line) of the Stoer Group with breccio-conglomerates resting on Lewisian gneisses (lower left), Clachtoll graveyard, north-west Scotland.

Basal conglomerates with Lewisian-derived clasts pass upwards into cross-bedded sandstones which are intercalated with aeolian sandstones. Palaeocurrents indicate both an easterly and westerly derivation of these sediments, and an age for diagenesis of *c.* 1199 Ma has been obtained on limestones within the sequence. The presence of normal faults in the Lewisian basement, which were active at the time of sedimentation, suggest that deposition of the Stoer Group was linked to major rifting during crustal stretching. On a broader scale, it has been suggested that these events may be linked to a major phase of crustal extension that led to rifting apart of Baltica from Laurentia at this time.

3.5.2 The Grenville Orogeny

On a global scale, the Mesoproterozoic Grenville Orogeny resulted from plate convergence associated with the formation of a major Mesoproterozoic supercontinent called Rodinia. Evidence for the Grenville Orogeny, most of which is preserved in Canada, is provided by exposures from the basement rocks in the Glenelg inlier of north-west Scotland and the Annagh Gneiss Complex of north-west Ireland. Rocks of the Glenelg inlier (for location see Figure 3.3b) occur in fault-bounded contact with rocks of the Neoproterozoic Moine Supergroup (described in Section 3.6.2). The basement gneisses and mafic inclusions, thought to have been dykes or sills, contain relicts of high-pressure eclogite-facies mineral assemblages metamorphosed at $750 \pm 25\,°C$ and $c.\ 1600\,MPa$. These conditions correspond to depths of $c.\ 55\,km$ (Figure 2.6) and can only have been achieved as a result of considerable crustal thickening during collisional orogeny resulting from plate convergence. Isotopic dating of metamorphic minerals has given an age of $c.\ 1110–1082\,Ma$ for this event, corresponding to the Mesoproterozoic Grenville Orogeny. Additional evidence for Grenvillian events is provided by ages of $c.\ 1100–1000\,Ma$ obtained from syn-tectonic granites that intrude the Annagh Gneiss Complex (Figure 3.9). Indirect evidence for the extent of possible Grenville-age rocks south-east of the Highland Boundary Fault (Figure 3.3a) comes from fragments of deep crustal rocks that were brought to the surface by Carboniferous volcanic activity in the Midland Valley. Certain of the volcanic vents contain granulite-facies blocks that have given ages of $c.\ 1100–1000\,Ma$, coincident with the timing of Grenville orogenic crustal thickening

3.6 Neoproterozoic events

The period from $c.\ 1000\,Ma$ to $c.\ 800\,Ma$ was dominated by the accumulation of thick sedimentary sequences (the Sleat and Torridon Groups) in extensive basins. The sediments were derived from the erosion of the Grenville mountain belt. In the Northern and Central Highlands, crustal or lithospheric extension at this time culminated in the emplacement of bimodal (mafic and felsic) magmatic suites at $c.\ 870\,Ma$, and was brought to an end by the Knoydartian Orogeny at $c.\ 840–780\,Ma$.

3.6.1 Early Neoproterozoic continental sedimentation: the Sleat and Torridon Groups

Early Neoproterozoic continental sedimentation is represented by the Sleat and Torridon Groups (sometimes referred to informally as the Torridonian), which outcrop along the north-western seaboard of Scotland (Figure 3.3b). The oldest rocks belong to the Sleat Group and comprise $c.\ 3.5\,km$ of coarse-grained fluvial and deltaic sandstones with minor marine and lacustrine deposits. Although the base is unexposed, the Sleat Group is thought to lie unconformably on the Lewisian basement. The Sleat Group passes transitionally upwards into the overlying red arkosic sandstones of the Torridon Group.

The Torridon Group overlaps the underlying Stoer Group and in places rests unconformably on an eroded Lewisian landscape with $c.\ 600\,m$ of topography. The lowest formation, the Diabeg, is a succession of red breccias, grey sandstones and shales, deposited in an alluvial fan environment. The uppermost Torridon formations (the Applecross and Aultbea Formations) comprise coarse clastic sandstones and were deposited from major alluvial braided-river systems that prograded eastwards. The petrology of the clasts within the Torridon Group suggests that they were derived from the erosion of Lewisian gneisses and supracrustal rocks. The youngest date obtained from detrital zircons from the

Applecross Formation is *c.* 1060 Ma, so this constrains the maximum depositional age of this Formation. Furthermore, Rb–Sr ages from the Diabeg and Applecross Formations are interpreted to date diagenesis at *c.* 994 Ma and *c.* 977 Ma respectively. Data from detrital minerals also indicate a distal source that comprised remnants of Archaean to Mesoproterozoic basement rocks that had been affected by high-grade Grenvillian metamorphism. These data confirm a post-*c.* 1100 Ma depositional age for the Torridon Group.

3.6.2   Early Neoproterozoic marine sedimentation: the Moine Supergroup

The Moine Supergroup is a thick succession of strongly deformed and metamorphosed siltstones, mudstones and sandstones that outcrop extensively between the Moine Thrust and the Great Glen Fault (Figure 3.3b). The Moine Supergroup was deposited unconformably on *c.* 2800 Ma Archaean basement gneisses, which occur as infolded and tectonically interleaved inliers within Moine rocks as a result of extensive Caledonian tectonism (Figure. 3.3b). An upper age limit for deposition (*c.* 1000 Ma) is provided by the age of the youngest detrital minerals dated so far. A lower age limit is provided by the age of the oldest igneous rocks that intrude the sediments (*c.* 873 Ma, see Section 3.6.4).

The Moine Supergroup is subdivided into the Morar, Glenfinnan and Loch Eil Groups. The Morar and Loch Eil Groups are shallow marine sediments that were probably deposited in NNE–SSW-trending half grabens that were bounded by major ESE-dipping faults (Figure 3.12).

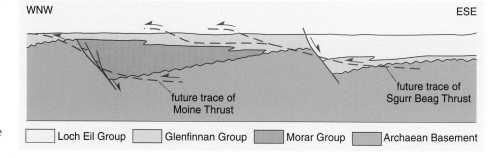

Figure 3.12 Schematic illustration of the original stratigraphic relationship of the Moine Supergroup basins. The positions of the major Caledonian thrusts that subsequently dissected the basins are shown.

Palaeocurrent data suggest that the basins were sourced from the south. Early rift sedimentation in the Morar Group may have been followed by transgressive deposition of the Glenfinnan Group. The Loch Eil Group conformably overlies the Glenfinnan Group and its asymmetric facies distribution and westward thickening of sediments in half grabens suggests a return to more active rifting. Amphibolites in the Loch Eil and Glenfinnan Groups are thought to represent basic igneous rocks intruded during rifting.

Provenance studies reveal that detrital zircons from Moine metasediments have ages ranging from *c.* 1900 Ma to *c.* 1000 Ma, precluding derivation from the Archaean Lewisian Complex. Taking the age data together with sedimentary structures in the Moine metasediments that indicate sediment transport from the south, the Palaeo- and Mesoproterozoic rocks of the Rhinns and Annagh Complexes are one possible source.

There has been much debate over whether or not the Torridonian and Moine rocks were deposited as continental and marine sequences in the same basin. Although isotopic constraints on the Sleat and Torridon Groups and the Moine Supergroup indicate that they are time equivalent (Figure 3.1), the rather different source regions, as indicated by the detrital mineral suites, suggest that they may have been deposited in separate basins.

3.6.3   The Dava and Glen Banchor Successions

The Dava and Glen Banchor Successions (formerly the Central Highland Migmatite Complex) are a sequence of psammites and pelites that outcrop south-east of the Great Glen Fault (Figure 3.3b). The rocks strongly resemble part of the Moine Supergroup and have been correlated by some workers. The detrital zircon ages are similar to those from the Moine Supergroup, which suggests that the sediments were derived from a similar source region. A radiometric age of *c.* 840 Ma obtained from the migmatitic gneisses is interpreted as dating metamorphism (discussed in Section 3.6.5), so it only provides a minimum age of deposition. These rocks are therefore probably Neoproterozoic in age, and as such may be a possible time equivalent of the Moine Supergroup (Figure 3.1).

3.6.4   Extension-related magmatism

A suite of deformed and metamorphosed granitic bodies, collectively termed the West Highland Granitic Gneisses, intrude the Moine Supergroup (Figure. 3.3b). These granites are thought to have been formed as a result of partial melting of Moine rocks at a deeper crustal level, and recent isotopic dating of several of these bodies indicates an age of *c.* 873 Ma for their emplacement. The granites are cut by a series of metagabbros which have yielded similar ages (*c.* 873 Ma). The metagabbros are spatially related to a regional suite of MORB-type metadolerites, and these basaltic rocks were thought to have been emplaced during regional extension. The mafic magmas may have provided the heat source necessary to melt the Moine rocks and generate the granitic gneisses.

3.6.5   Evidence for a Neoproterozoic (Knoydartian) Orogeny?

A growing body of isotopic-dating evidence now points to the existence of a major orogenic episode in the Neoproterozoic, an event referred to as the Knoydartian Orogeny. The Moine Supergroup is widely veined by pegmatites (Figure 3.13), with isotopic dating yielding an age range of *c.* 827–780 Ma. Field relations indicate that these pegmatites were emplaced during regional ductile deformation and metamorphism.

Figure 3.13 Deformed and folded granitic pegmatite within Moine metasediments, Morar Peninsula, north-west Scotland.

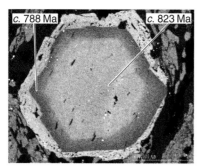

Figure 3.14 Chemical zoning of garnet from the Morar Peninsula, Scotland, is shown in this X-ray map obtained using a scanning electron microscope. Calcium concentration is depicted on a grey scale: pale denotes high concentration, dark denotes low concentration. The garnet shows three chemical zones which clearly indicate a well-formed garnet that is overgrown by a later high-Ca ragged rim. The high-Ca inner cores have given ages of *c.* 823 Ma whereas the low-Ca outer cores gave *c.* 788 Ma. The high-Ca garnet overgrowth is probably related to a later phase of garnet growth during the Caledonian Orogeny. Width of image *c.* 1 cm.

In addition, garnets from Morar Group metasediments have been dated by isotopic methods. Radiometric dating of the cores of garnet crystals that show multiple growth phases indicated initial growth at *c.* 823 Ma, whereas the rims yielded *c.* 788 Ma (Figure 3.14), implying that garnet growth lasted some 35 million years. Conditions of metamorphism at the time of garnet rim growth have been estimated at 1000–1200 MPa and 575–625 °C. These metamorphic conditions could not have been produced by crustal extension and are therefore linked to a significant crustal thickening event, the Knoydartian Orogeny.

To the south-east of the Great Glen Fault, in the Dava and Glen Banchor Successions, radiometric ages obtained on zircons from the metasediments are interpreted as dating partial melting and migmatite formation at *c.* 840 Ma. The migmatites were subsequently deformed in a series of ductile shear zones collectively known as the Grampian Shear Zone (Figure 3.3b). Some of the shear zones incorporate syn-tectonic granitic pegmatites and veins; the ages of the shear zones are considered to be *c.* 806 Ma, based on the dating of monazite that crystallized during metamorphism. These ages therefore record pegmatite crystallization and metamorphic mineral growth. The Dava and Glen Banchor Successions are unconformably overlain by rocks of the Dalradian Supergroup (the subject of Section 4) which show no evidence of having been affected by the deformation and metamorphic events that are assigned to the Knoydartian event.

From the available evidence it is concluded that the Moine Supergroup and Dava and Glen Banchor Successions were deformed and metamorphosed during the Knoydartian Orogeny at *c.* 840–780 Ma. Although there is mounting evidence for the Knoydartian Orogeny, it is a good example of an orogenic episode for which there is only fragmentary evidence. As such, its broader geological significance is uncertain at present.

3.7   Summary of Section 3

- The Proterozoic *c.* 2500–750 Ma evolution of Britain and Ireland was characterized by periods of rifting and extension, and episodes of plate convergence and collision.

- Periodic crustal extension led to the accumulation of thick sedimentary successions in rift-related basins. On a larger scale, extreme extension led to rupturing of the crust, the intrusion of dyke swarms and formation of oceanic crust. These periods are linked to separation and eventual break-up of major continental masses (supercontinents).

- Plate convergence and collision led to the closure of ocean basins, the assembly of continental masses by terrane accretion and crustal growth by magma addition at subduction zones.

- During collision, rock units were subjected to intense deformation and the resulting crustal thickening led to regional metamorphism.

4 Continental break up and opening of the Iapetus Ocean

4.1 Introduction

In the period from c. 2500–750 Ma, plate collisions led to the formation of a series of supercontinents which periodically broke up to form large oceanic basins. By c. 750 Ma, the main continental blocks were once again amalgamated, forming the Vendian supercontinent. Subsequently, the Vendian supercontinent split apart into the smaller continental masses of Laurentia, Baltica and Gondwana, a process which led to the formation of the Iapetus Ocean (Figure 1.5). During this period, extensive sedimentary deposits accumulated on the passive continental margins until extension and rifting were brought to an end by the early Palaeozoic Caledonian Orogeny.

This Section presents the evidence for a prolonged period of extension, rifting and sedimentation along the margin of the continent of Laurentia that lasted from c. 800 Ma into early Ordovician times. Firstly, we describe the evolution of the Dalradian Supergroup, a late Neoproterozoic to early Ordovician sedimentary succession that was extensively metamorphosed during the Caledonian Orogeny and is now exposed in the Grampian Highlands. Secondly, we describe the Cambrian–Ordovician sedimentary succession that is exposed in the Hebridean Terrane.

Figure 4.1 (a) Outcrop distribution of Cambrian–Ordovician sedimentary rocks of the Caledonian Foreland. (b) Simplified outcrop map of the Dalradian rocks of Scotland. The lineaments are major structural features that were active during Dalradian sedimentation.

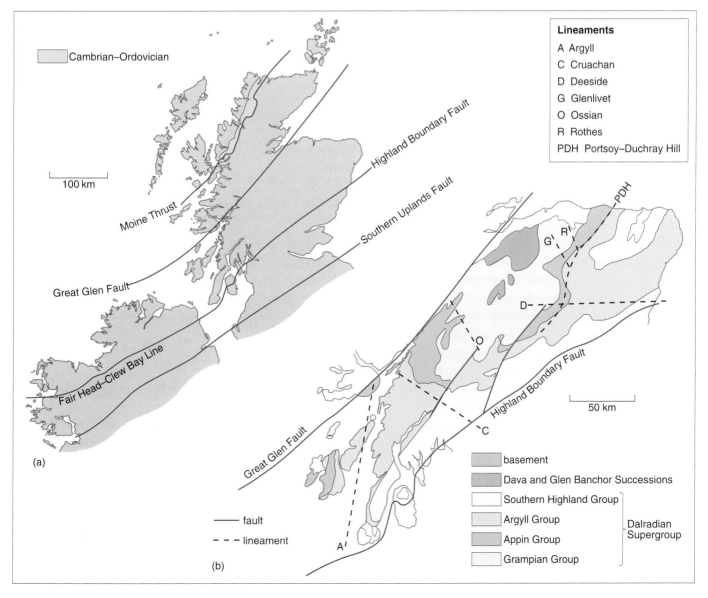

4.2 The Dalradian Supergroup

The Dalradian Supergroup is found between the Great Glen Fault and the Highland Boundary Fault. The main outcrop pattern is controlled by the location of major folds and ductile faults or shear zones, known as slides, and also by the amount of post-folding uplift that occurred near the end of the Caledonian Orogeny. Late post-orogenic brittle faults have displaced boundaries, often by tens of kilometres. In the central Grampian region, a series of NE–SW-trending faults with significant sinistral displacements offset the regional pattern, and significant vertical displacements occurred along several transverse NW–SE-trending faults. Fortuitously for geologists, this pattern reveals a wide range of exposure levels.

4.2.1   Dalradian sedimentary basins: seeing through metamorphism

Despite complex deformation and metamorphism during the Caledonian Orogeny, the sedimentary evolution and pre-Iapetan context of the Dalradian basin have been established. The intensity of Caledonian metamorphism and deformation varies across the Grampian Highlands, but in areas of low metamorphic grade, sedimentological studies have revealed much about the palaeogeography and the nature and origin of the sedimentary sequences. Furthermore, petrological and chemical studies of contemporaneous igneous rocks have provided additional constraints on tectonic settings. In areas of high metamorphic grade, the original sedimentary nature of the rocks has been more difficult to establish because recrystallization and deformation have partly destroyed the sedimentological evidence. Despite this, some rock types such as psammites (metamorphosed muddy sandstones) and quartzites retain evidence of primary sedimentary structures (Figure 4.2), whereas coarse recrystallization and mineral growth has eradicated all such evidence from pelitic and semipelitic lithologies (metamorphosed mudstones and sandy mudstones). As a result, studies of the evolution of the Dalradian Supergroup are based on large-scale approaches to sedimentation and basin evolution.

Figure 4.2   Grampian Group quartzites, in the A9 road cutting at Clunes, 20 km north-west of Pitlochry. The cross-stratification demonstrates that these sediments are the right way up.

4.2.2 Primary rock types and terminology

The Dalradian Supergroup is a metamorphosed succession of clastic sediments (marine sandstones, siltstones, and mudstones) and limestones with some volcanic rocks. The names used to describe individual units depend on metamorphic grade. To describe rocks of low metamorphic grade, many sedimentary rock terms are used (e.g. sandstone, siltstone) whereas, as metamorphic grade increases, metamorphic terms (e.g. pelite, semipelite, psammite and quartzite) are used to indicate the original composition of the sediment. To these, some textural terms have been added (e.g. slate, phyllite, schist or gneiss). The metamorphosed carbonate rocks are referred to as limestones, dolomites or dolostones. Metamorphosed igneous rocks are classified, where possible, on the basis of their non-metamorphosed equivalents (e.g. metabasalt, metagabbro). Where the non-metamorphosed equivalent cannot be identified, the term amphibolite, hornblende schist or gneiss is often used.

4.2.3 Lithostratigraphic subdivisions of the Dalradian Supergroup

The total thickness of the Dalradian succession is difficult to work out as it has been tectonically thickened and thinned by later orogenesis. There is also no continuous section. Piecing all the evidence together, it has been estimated that the Dalradian succession is at least 25 km thick. As with other major sedimentary successions, the Dalradian Supergroup is divided on the basis of a hierarchy of scales, which are, from largest to smallest, Group, Subgroup and Formation. Hence the Dalradian Supergroup is subdivided into the Grampian, Appin, Argyll and Southern Highland Groups (Figure 4.3).

In most parts of the Dalradian Supergroup a consistent stratigraphy has been established on the basis of distinctive lithologies and lithological associations cropping out in a consistent order, as determined from sedimentary and igneous way-up structures. However, problems arise where rapid lateral sedimentary facies changes and tectonic complexity occur, such as where very high tectonic strains excise or severely attenuate parts of the succession. Because of such difficulties, widespread correlation at Formation level across the Dalradian basin is not reliable. Correlation at Group level is based on distinctive and key lithologies that have been recognized and traced throughout the Grampian Highlands and into Ireland and Shetland, a distance of up to c. 700 km. These distinctive lithologies are thought to represent regionally significant changes in the evolution of the basin. Correlation at Subgroup level has been successful in some areas.

4.3 Dalradian sedimentation and tectonics

Reconstructing the geological evolution of the Dalradian basin depends on studies of the Dalradian sedimentary succession, so this Section provides an overview of the key stratigraphic observations upon which the synthesis given in Section 4.4 relies.

The Grampian Group is mainly composed of micaceous to quartzose psammites and semipelites (7–8 km thick). The lowermost Glenshirra Subgroup consists of psammites and metaconglomerates. Sedimentary structures in these rocks indicate deposition in shallow marine environments, and the progressive westward thickening and coarsening of strata indicate deposition possibly adjacent to the basin margin. The onset of widespread extension and rifting led to basin deepening and the influx of turbiditic sandstones of the Corrieyairick Subgroup. Lateral facies changes and thickness variations point to the existence of a series of NE–SW-trending major syn-sedimentary faults (Figure 4.4a,b).

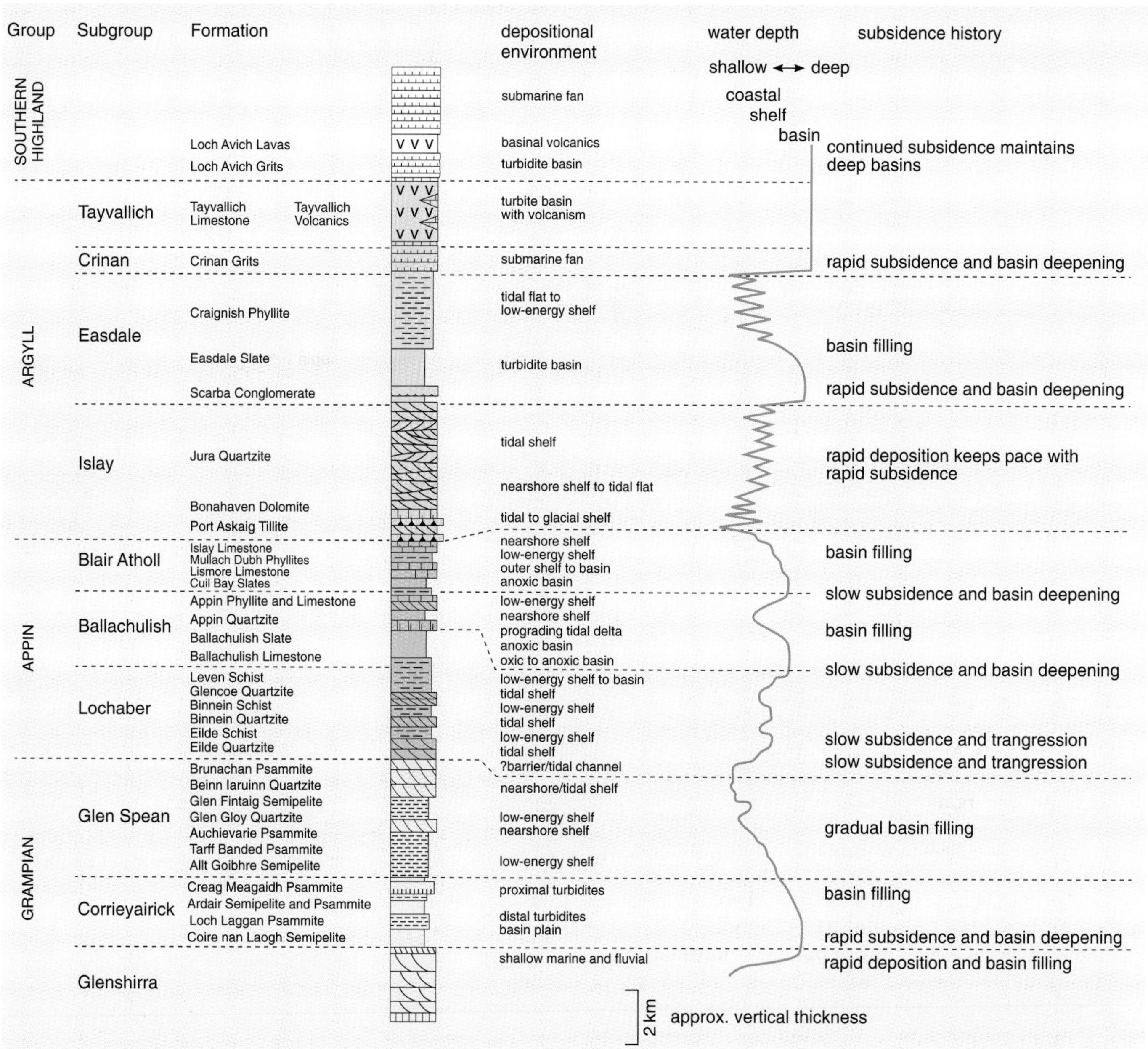

Figure 4.3 Dalradian stratigraphy and sedimentary evolution, based on successions from the western Central Highlands. Chronostratigraphic division of the Dalradian is discussed in Section 4.5.

The overlying semipelites, psammites and quartzites of the Glen Spean Subgroup are interpreted to represent SE-prograding deltaic and shallow marine tidal sequences (Figure 4.4b). The overstep onto older strata constrains the basin margins and is related to intrabasinal structural highs that were active and uplifting during Grampian and early Appin Group times (Figure 4.4c).

Quartzites, limestones, pelites and semipelites belonging to the Appin Group were deposited on a marine shelf. Sediments of the lowermost parts of the Lochaber Subgroup are interfingered with those of the Grampian Group as a result of renewed marine transgression, such that the Appin Group has a transitional base. Sedimentary structures indicate deposition on a periodically emergent tidal shelf, and SW to NE sedimentary influx. The upper parts of the Appin Group, the Ballachulish and Blair Atholl Subgroups, are dominated by extensive offshore carbonates and anoxic mudstones – sequences that point to a period of low sediment supply and basin widening. The top of the Appin Group, the Islay Limestone, indicates a return to shallow intertidal deposition, and sedimentary structures indicate a warm arid environment. Rapid lateral facies changes in the upper part of the Appin Group imply syn-depositional faulting

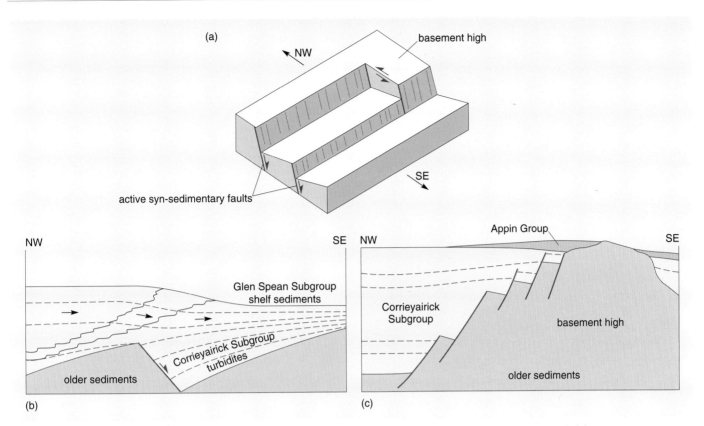

Figure 4.4 Schematic summary of basin evolution during deposition of the Grampian Group in Scotland. (a) Basement configuration as indicated by variations in facies thickness. (b) Syn-rift deposition of the Corrieyairick Subgroup produced thickness variations. Arrows show the progradation of post-rift deposits of the Glen Spean Subgroup. (c) Sedimentation against an intrabasinal structural high in Grampian times. The older sediments are those of the Dava and Glen Banchor Successions. Note that the faults on the margin of the high were active at different times during sedimentation.

and the development of half-graben basins that accommodated the deposition of these essentially shallow-water deposits (Figure 4.5). Palaeocurrent data and lateral thickness variations suggest SW to NE sedimentary influx into a series of NE–SW-trending basins during a phase of more active rifting.

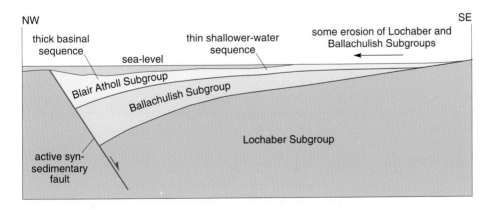

Figure 4.5 Syn-rift sedimentation and basin evolution during the deposition of the upper Appin Group. Note the thinning of facies and erosion of lower Subgroups on the rift shoulders indicating they were active and uplifting during deposition.

The base of the Argyll Group is marked by a marine tillite, or boulder bed deposit – the Port Askaig Tillite (correlated with the Schiehallion Boulder Bed in Perthshire). The sediments comprise c. 750 m thickness of sandstones, conglomerates, dolostones, siltstones and numerous boulder beds (diamictites).

The boulder beds were either deposited from grounded ice sheets, or, given the presence of dropstones, were derived from floating ice (Figure 4.6).

Figure 4.6   Diamictite from the Port Askaig Tillite, Garvellach Islands.

The overlying Bonahaven Dolomite indicates a return to warmer conditions. The Jura Quartzite represents a marine transgression heralded by the influx of thick (c. 5 km) tidal-shelf sands. Thick conglomerates, turbidites and muds of the Easdale Subgroup marked the initiation of shelf deepening, due to rapid crustal stretching. Sharp lateral thickness variations were caused by deposition of sediment in a series of fault-controlled NE–SW-trending basins. Intrabasinal structural highs are marked by local thinning, lateral facies changes and erosion or non-deposition of sediments. These highs correspond to long-lasting NW–SE- and NE–SW-trending lineaments. Regional crustal extension in the deep basins allowed seawater to penetrate down reactivated faults, leaching underlying sediments through the creation of hydrothermal convection cells and forming brines containing barium and base metals. Where the mineral-rich brines came to the surface and ponded on the sea-floor, barium and base-metal mineral deposits such as those found at Foss, near Aberfeldy, in Perthshire (a major source of the mineral barytes) were formed. The deep-water basins eventually filled, and shallower-water conditions returned. Renewed rapid subsidence is indicated by the turbidite fan deposits of the Crinan Grits. The uppermost part of the Argyll Group, the Tayvallich Subgroup, includes the Tayvallich Volcanics, which comprise pillow basalts and volcanic ashes interbedded with deep-water turbiditic limestones and pelites, and cross-cut by basic sills and dykes. Sedimentary structures indicate that the sediments were wet at the time of dyke intrusion. The Tayvallich Volcanics are mostly tholeiitic in composition and probably resulted from mantle melting during crustal rifting.

The north-eastern limit of abundant volcanism coincides with a major NW–SE-oriented structure known as the Cruachan lineament (for location, see Figure 4.1). The Cruachan lineament is thought to correspond to a major structure in the basement that is transverse to the main structural trend. On the basis that many of the basic dykes on Jura have a NW–SE trend, implying NE–SW extension, it has been suggested that the Cruachan lineament bounds a pull-apart basin that developed as a result of transtension (Figure 4.7).

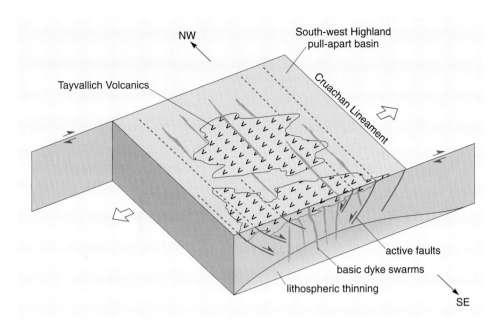

NW

South-west Highland pull-apart basin

Cruachan Lineament

Tayvallich Volcanics

active faults

basic dyke swarms

lithospheric thinning

SE

Figure 4.7 Schematic illustration of the South-west Highland pull-apart basin active during late Argyll times.

The Southern Highland Group marks the top of the exposed Dalradian succession and consists mainly of mudstones, sandstones and grits. These clastic sediments are interbedded with basic volcanics – in the form of pillow basalts and 'green beds' that are thought to represent volcaniclastic deposits – and deep-water trilobite-bearing limestones and mudstones. The clastic sediments are interpreted as submarine fans and indicate a return to rapid basin deepening. The Southern Highland Group sediments were deposited on an outer continental margin.

4.4   Dalradian basin evolution

The lithostratigraphic, sedimentological and tectonic studies described in the previous Section revealed periods of basin deepening and shallowing that corresponded to phases of lithospheric stretching, rifting and subsidence. Faulting related to lithospheric stretching has been recognized as the principal control on sedimentation. It is envisaged that a series of SE-dipping fault blocks, bounded by normal faults, delimited individual basins on the continental shelf, exerting a direct impact on the shape and form of the sedimentary pile. In addition, the transverse structures termed lineaments (Figure 4.1), which have been identified on the basis of geophysical, stratigraphic and structural data, are also thought to have played a significant role. Major changes in Dalradian stratigraphy across some of these structures indicate that they had an influential control on sedimentation, as well as forming a focus for later Caledonian deformation and magmatism. The interpretation of these transverse structures as representing the site of pull-apart basins indicates that rifting may not have been simply a response to NW–SE extension.

The Dalradian Supergroup represents a segment of a significantly more extensive continental shelf sedimentary succession (Figure 4.8). Sedimentation initiated in a broad rift, floored by continental crust, that propagated north-eastwards to form a marine gulf. The Grampian and Appin Groups were deposited on a passive continental shelf on the north-west side of the rift. Continued extension and widening deepened the rift during deposition of the Argyll Group. The appearance of large volumes of volcanic material towards the

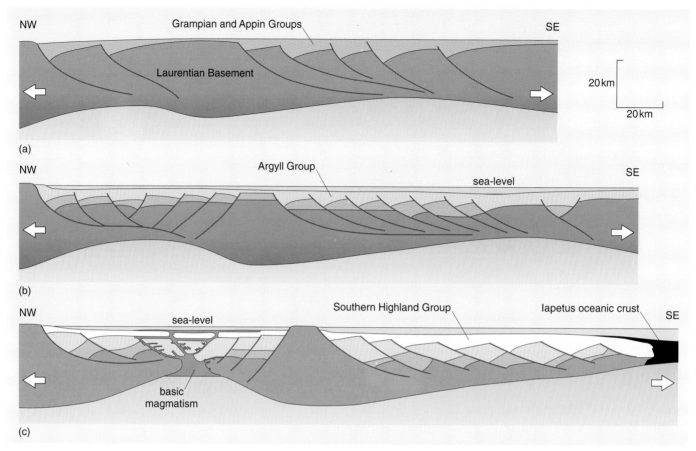

Figure 4.8   Schematic cross-sections showing the progressive development of the rifted Laurentian margin in Scotland in (a) late Appin Group times; (b) Argyll Group times; and (c) Southern Highland Group times.

top of the Argyll Group was associated with lithospheric thinning and rupturing of the continental crust. Volcanic activity continued during the deposition of the Southern Highland Group; this occurred on the rapidly subsiding continental margin which eventually broke up to form the Iapetus Ocean.

4.5   Age of the Dalradian Supergroup

The age of the Dalradian Supergroup is constrained by isotopic dating and occasional fossils, such that the essentially lithostratigraphic divisions of the Dalradian can be placed in a chronostratigraphic context as shown in Figure 4.9.

The lowermost part of the Dalradian is thought to onlap the older (>c. 840 Ma) metasediments of the Dava and Glen Banchor Successions. As we saw in Section 3.6.5, these metasediments were deformed and metamorphosed at c. 806 Ma, yet the Dalradian Supergroup shows no evidence of these events. These observations can only provide a maximum age of c. 806 Ma for deposition of the older parts of the Dalradian Supergroup (Grampian and Appin Groups).

The base of the Argyll Group is marked by the Port Askaig Tillite (Figure 4.9). A long-standing correlation of this important horizon with the c. 630–590 Ma Varangian tillites of Norway has recently been questioned, and on the basis of correlation with trends in global glaciations, a new age of c. 750–720 Ma (Sturtian) has been suggested. If this correlation is correct then the Loch na Cille Boulder Bed (Tayvallich Subgroup), which occurs near the top of the Argyll Group, must be significantly younger, and may therefore correlate with the c. 630–590 Ma Varangian tillites. Volcanics at the top of the Argyll Group (the Tayvallich Volcanics) provide better age constraints. An eruption age of

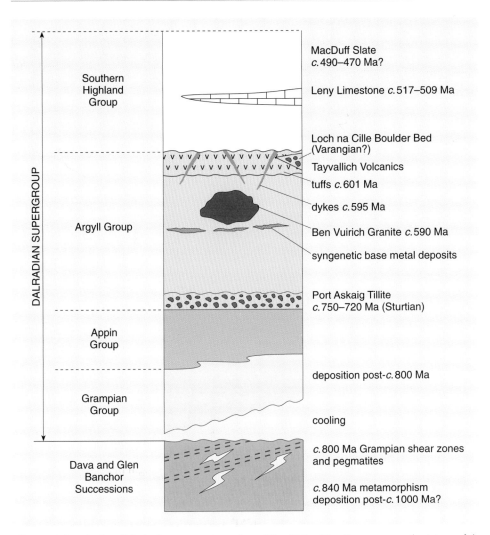

Figure 4.9 A simplified chronostratigraphy of the Dalradian Supergroup (not to scale).

c. 595 Ma has been obtained by dating zircons from a mafic dyke intrusive into the lavas, and a felsic tuff has yielded an age of *c.* 601 Ma. A further constraint is provided by the age of intrusion of the Ben Vuirich granite, dated by U–Pb methods on zircons at *c.* 590 Ma. The Ben Vuirich granite is one of several deformed and metamorphosed granites, collectively referred to as the Older Granites, which intrude Argyll Group sediments in the Pitlochry area. Structural studies of the Ben Vuirich granite have indicated that it was emplaced prior to regional orogenic (Grampian) deformation and metamorphism (described in Section 5). Given the overlap in the ages of the Older Granites and the Tayvallich Volcanics, it follows that granitic magmatism, basaltic volcanism and sedimentation must have been near-synchronous and occurred during continental rifting at *c.* 600–590 Ma. Taken together, these data indicate that the deposition of the Argyll Group spanned about 160 million years from *c.* 750–590 Ma.

Critical information on the biostratigraphic age of the highest preserved parts of the Southern Highland Group is provided by the presence of Early Cambrian trilobites, *c.* 517–509 Ma, within the Leny Limestone (found north of Callander). In north-east Scotland, in the Buchan area, the youngest sedimentary rocks of the Macduff Slate have yielded microfossils interpreted as Early Ordovician in age, although these identifications remain highly controversial and are not wholly accepted. If substantiated, these data would indicate that Dalradian sedimentation may have continued until *c.* 490–470 Ma.

Taking the available information at face value, it could be argued that the Dalradian Supergroup was deposited over a considerable time span (up to *c.* 330 million years) within the period from approximately 800 Ma to 470 Ma. However, a comparison of the Dalradian with well dated, better exposed and less deformed Neoproterozoic and Phanerozoic sedimentary basins, indicates that episodic rifting over such a considerable time span may be improbable. Moreover, it has been argued that the sedimentary facies represented in the lower part of the Dalradian (sub-Easdale Subgroup) are unlike those associated with extensional rifting, and are more akin to deposits formed in a convergent setting in foreland basins. It has also been suggested that several significant time gaps may exist in the succession, shedding some doubt on the validity of any model of continuous Dalradian deposition. Although at present controversial, the testing of these hypotheses and models, and the search for gaps in the Dalradian stratigraphy that may indicate major orogenic phases continues, and can only be achieved by detailed fieldwork in conjunction with integrated metamorphic and isotopic studies.

4.6 Cambrian–Ordovician shelf sedimentation in north-west Scotland

Cambrian–Ordovician sediments outcrop in a narrow belt immediately west of the Moine Thrust (Figure 4.1a). These rocks were deposited unconformably on the Lewisian Complex and Torridon Group; their present outcrop pattern is influenced by the effects of later deformation in the Moine Thrust Zone (Figure 4.10a). A restored cross-section indicates that the underlying Torridon Group lies in fault-bounded half-grabens that developed prior to deposition of the Cambrian succession (Figure 4.10b). The faults that bounded the half-grabens are thought to have developed in response to the late Neoproterozoic crustal extension which also generated the Dalradian sedimentary basins.

The Cambrian–Ordovician succession consists of a basal clastic sequence (250 m in thickness) that is overlain by over 1000 m of carbonates (Figure 4.11a). The succession overall records a marine transgression onto a stable shelf (Figure 4.11b).

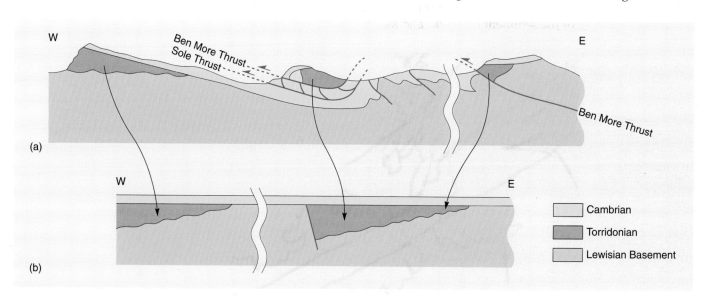

Figure 4.10 (a) Cross-section of the Caledonian Foreland and Moine Thrust Zone, from Canisp in the west to Ben More about 15 km to the east, in the Assynt area, north-west Scotland. (b) Restored cross-section showing Cambrian sediments deposited on a Lewisian and Torridonian surface.

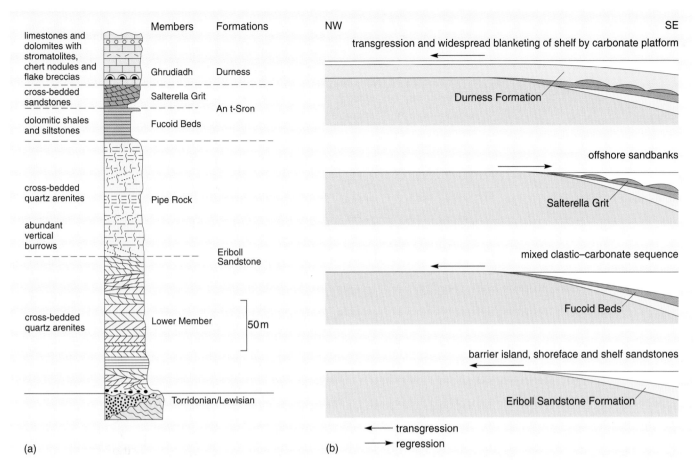

Figure 4.11 (a) Stratigraphy of the Cambrian–Ordovician of north-west Scotland. (b) Simplified sedimentary evolution of the Cambrian–Ordovician succession of north-west Scotland.

The lowermost part of the Eriboll Sandstone Formation comprises cross-bedded sandstones deposited in a barrier to tidal-shelf environment. The upper member, the Pipe Rock, gets its name from the abundant trace fossils formed as a result of pervasive burrowing of the sediment (*Skolithus* and *Monocraterion*) (Figure 4.12).

Figure 4.12 The upper member of the Eriboll Sandstone Formation, the Pipe Rock, showing distinctive burrows, Skaig Bridge, Loch Assynt shore. Scale indicated by coin.

The Eriboll Sandstone Formation is overlain by the An t-Sron Formation, comprising carbonate and clastic storm-dominated deposits (Fucoid Beds). Trilobites within this unit indicate an Early Cambrian age. The upper part (Salterella Grit) comprises coarse sandstones and grits that were probably deposited as offshore sandbanks during a short marine regression. Deposition of clastic sediments ceased and the platform was then swamped by a blanket of carbonates (the Durness Formation) that were deposited in a tidal flat to shallow subtidal environment. Rare fossils indicate an Early Ordovician age for these carbonates.

The shallow marine Cambrian–Ordovician succession of north-west Scotland developed contemporaneously with the deeper-water muds of the Southern Highland Group. It has been suggested that the shallow shelf conditions that existed in the early Dalradian trangressed north-westwards with time, as a result of continued rifting and a probable eustatic sea-level change.

4.7 Summary of Section 4

- Dalradian sedimentation occurred during a prolonged phase of lithospheric extension, lasting *c.* 330 million years (*c.* 800–470 Ma), which eventually led to formation of the Iapetus Ocean.

- The Grampian, Appin and Argyll Groups were deposited on a passive continental shelf. Progressive instability of the basin through time led to deposition of deeper-water facies. Sedimentation was controlled by the development of a series of NE–SW-oriented fault-bounded basins. Transverse structures may have controlled both sedimentation and the locus of volcanic activity.

- The emplacement of large volumes of basic magma resulted from the rupturing of the continental crust.

- Basic volcanics and glacial deposits (tillites) are potentially important stratigraphic markers and also provide critical constraints on the timing of Dalradian sedimentation.

- Cambrian–Ordovician shallow-water shelf sedimentation in north-west Scotland was contemporaneous with deposition of deep-water, outer-shelf, muds of the Southern Highland Group.

5 Arc–continent collision: the Grampian phase of the Caledonian Orogeny

5.1 Introduction

Section 4 described how a prolonged period of lithospheric extension led to the development of a passive margin on the southern flanks of Laurentia. Eventually (in late Neoproterozoic to early Palaeozoic times), extension led to rupturing of the crust, and the opening, to the south of Laurentia, of the Iapetus Ocean. The destruction of the Iapetus Ocean took place later in the early Palaeozoic (Section 1.2) as a result of subduction. The subduction culminated in plate collisions accompanied by mountain-building events known as the Caledonian Orogeny. The Caledonian Orogeny comprised three distinct phases: the Grampian phase (c. 480–465 Ma), an intermediate phase (c. 465–435 Ma) for which there is no formal name, and the Scandian phase (c. 435–390 Ma). This Section and Sections 6 and 8 deal with the extent, nature and timing of these phases.

Figure 5.1   A tectonic model for the Grampian phase of the Caledonian Orogeny. (a) A pre-Grampian stage showing the opening of the Iapetus Ocean and Dalradian sedimentation on rifted Laurentian crust. (b) S-directed subduction formed an island arc complex on continental crust. (c) Initial collision led to narrowing of oceanic tracts, the obduction of ophiolites, and crustal thickening, deformation and metamorphism on the Laurentian margin. (d) Continued collision resulted in folding and underthrusting of the Laurentian margin, and a N-dipping subduction zone.

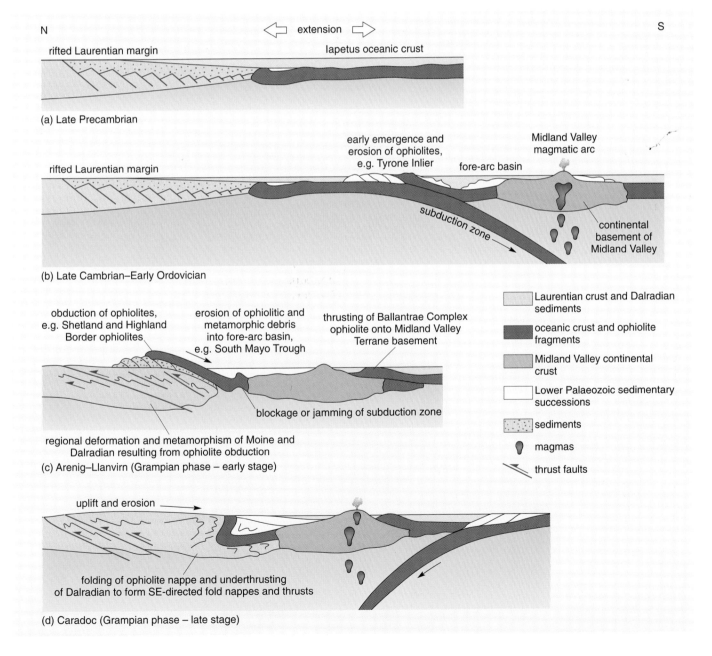

The Grampian phase of the Caledonian Orogeny resulted from the collision between the Laurentian margin and an oceanic subduction zone and island arc complex that had developed in the Iapetus Ocean during early Cambrian to early Ordovician times (Figure 5.1). The sequence of events depicted in Figure 5.1 is explained in this Section, with the evidence coming from a variety of sources. Section 5.2 considers the evidence for the existence of an ocean and the nature and timing of its closure and destruction during the Grampian phase. This relies on the study of ophiolite fragments. Section 5.3 examines the deformation suffered by the Dalradian rocks and relates it to the collision of crustal blocks, and the crust's response to crustal shortening. Section 5.4 considers the metamorphism of the Dalradian rocks that occurred in association with the collision. Finally, Section 5.5 provides a brief summary of these events.

5.2   Ocean closure during the Grampian phase

5.2.1   Ophiolites and the evidence for obduction: a Grampian suture zone?

Figure 5.2   Terrane map of the northern British Isles showing the distributions of ophiolite fragments and rocks of island arc affinity that were accreted to the Laurentian margin during the Grampian phase.

The recognition of ophiolites within an orogenic belt is important because they represent fragments of oceanic lithosphere caught up between converging plates. For example, in the Himalaya, ophiolite fragments outcrop in a line marking an

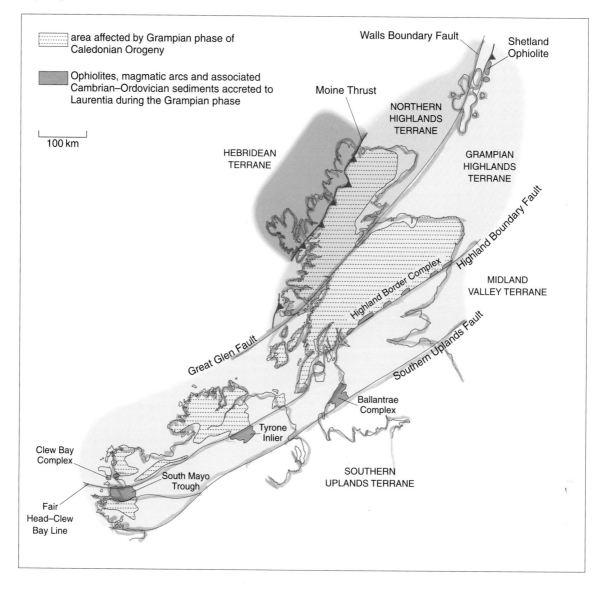

ancient subduction or suture zone that separates two crustal blocks or continents with contrasting geological histories. The distribution of the ophiolite fragments and related rocks of oceanic affinity in northern Britain is illustrated in Figure 5.2.

Most of the smaller fragments lie in a line along or close to the Highland Boundary Fault – Fair Head–Clew Bay Line (e.g. the Clew Bay Complex, Tyrone inlier and the Highland Border Complex). This fault is thought to indicate the position of an ancient suture zone. Two larger bodies, the Shetland ophiolite and the Ballantrae Complex lie far from this suture zone and their position merits further investigation.

The Shetland ophiolite lies immediately to the east of the Walls Boundary Fault, a structure interpreted as the northerly extension of the Great Glen Fault (Figure 5.2). The ophiolite itself comprises basic and ultrabasic igneous rocks and is contained within two thrust nappes that tectonically overlie metasedimentary rocks attributed to the Dalradian Supergroup (Figure 5.3).

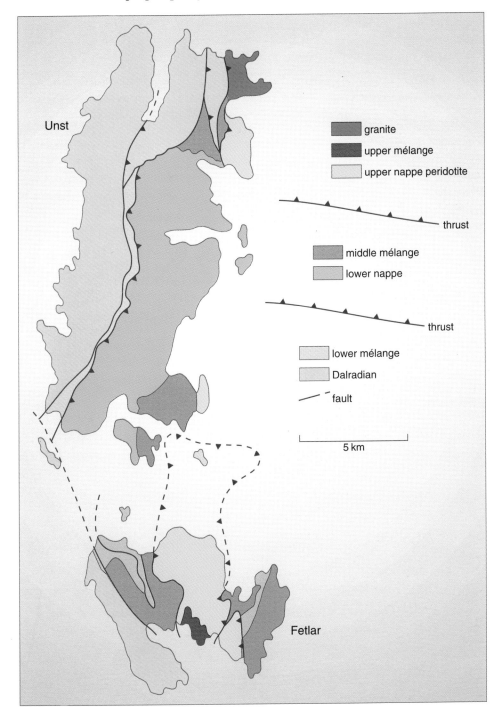

Figure 5.3 Simplified geological map of Unst and Fetlar. The key shows the packages of rocks that are separated by thrusts, with the Shetland ophiolite comprising the lower and upper nappes.

The lower nappe contains peridotites, pyroxenites and dunites overlain by gabbros and a sheeted dyke complex. The upper nappe is composed of peridotites. The occurrence of ophiolitic nappes in thrust contact with Dalradian metasediments suggests that the oceanic crust had been tectonically emplaced by thrusting onto the continental crust – a process called obduction. The position of the complex more than 100 km west of the proposed suture (Figure 5.2) would be consistent with significant tectonic transport from east to west. Radiometric dating of granite intruded during crystallization of the complex gives an age of *c.* 492 Ma (Tremadoc) and provides a date for formation of the oceanic crust at a mid-ocean ridge. The Shetland ophiolite therefore provides structural evidence for the obduction by thrusting of *c.* 492 Ma-old oceanic crust onto the Laurentian margin. The ophiolite is interpreted as an eroded remnant of a much larger ophiolite-bearing thrust nappe.

The Tyrone inlier (Figure 5.2) comprises gabbros, a sheeted dyke complex and pillow basalts, and is interpreted as an ophiolite fragment. The complex has been thrust towards the north-west onto an older sequence of schists and gneisses of unknown age. A tonalite intruded into the inlier has been dated at *c.* 471 Ma and contains more ancient zircons that have possibly been derived from underlying Proterozoic rocks. The tonalite must therefore have intruded the ophiolite after it was obducted onto continental crust.

The Ballantrae Complex is located on the southern margin of the Midland Valley (Figure 5.2). It comprises serpentinized peridotites with minor gabbro and trondhjemite, overlain by basaltic pillow lavas. The ophiolite has a metamorphic sole composed of schist that formed during emplacement of the ophiolite. Radiometric dating of amphiboles from the schists has given an age of *c.* 478 Ma. This age is interpreted as dating cooling following obduction. The underlying rocks are not exposed.

The Highland Border Complex is a series of low-grade metamorphic rocks that occur in a series of discontinuously exposed fault-bounded slivers along the Highland Boundary Fault (Figure 5.2). The complex is divided into four distinct assemblages. The oldest comprises serpentinites, hornblende schists and pillow basalts, which are interpreted as remnants of an ophiolite, and are unconformably overlain by a second assemblage containing conglomerates and shallow-water dolomitic limestones. Faunas indicate an Arenig age for this assemblage. The third assemblage contains an oceanic sequence of altered pillow lavas (Figure 5.4), tuffs, breccias, black shales, cherts and sandy turbidites (late Arenig to Llanvirn in age). The fourth and youngest assemblage (of Caradoc age) comprises limestones and sandstones.

Figure 5.4 Pillow lavas from the Highland Border Complex near Stonehaven.

The history and tectonic significance of the Highland Border Complex is highly controversial, and two hypotheses have been proposed. The first is that the complex represents a fragment of an entirely separate ocean basin that lay to the south of Laurentia. This model is based on the evidence that the fourth assemblage (of Caradoc age, c. 462–449 Ma) must have been deposited after the c. 480–465 Ma Grampian phase. The second hypothesis is that the complex represents a series of slices of the uppermost part of the Dalradian Supergroup and an ophiolite. This model is based on observations that the low-grade metasedimentary rocks and the ophiolite all carry similar Grampian-age structures to those in adjacent Dalradian rocks. More work is required to resolve this issue.

5.2.2 Evidence for an ancient magmatic arc

The Ballantrae Complex is unconformably overlain by Ordovician (Llanvirn to Caradoc, c. 470–450 Ma) fluvial, deltaic and marine sediments. Lateral facies changes indicate that deposition was fault-controlled, with successively younger strata overlapping northwards onto the ophiolite complex (Figure 5.5). Conglomerates sourced from the north-west were deposited in submarine fans; in the south-east they are overlain by deep-water mudstones and sandstones. These grade northwards into shallower-water mudstones, sandstones and limestones.

The provenance (Box 3.1) of clasts within the conglomeratic units is of particular interest in reconstructing the palaeogeography. The conglomerates were locally sourced, with clasts of basic and ultrabasic material derived from the Ballantrae ophiolite, as well as clasts of granitic to intermediate igneous rocks and occasional low-grade schists. The granites are calc-alkaline in composition, suggesting derivation from a magmatic arc. Isotopic ages obtained on these clasts range from c. 560–450 Ma. These data point to the existence of a Cambrian to early Ordovician magmatic arc that lay somewhere to the north or north-west of the Southern Uplands Fault.

⬤ How do the ages of the igneous clasts in the conglomerate compare with the depositional age of the conglomerate itself?

⬤ These ages overlap, implying that the island arc complex was still forming by subduction in the Early Ordovician, and at the same time being actively eroded.

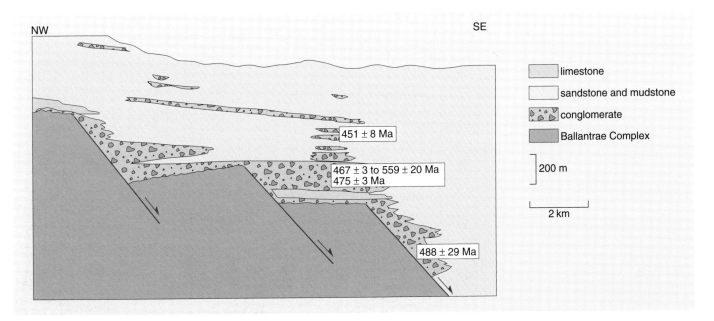

Figure 5.5   Details of the Ordovician sedimentary successions that overlie the Ballantrae Complex. Note the presence of extensional faults that were active during deposition of the sediments. The diagram also shows the range of radiometric ages obtained from granitic clasts within the conglomerates.

A similar picture emerges from north-west Ireland where the rocks of the South Mayo Trough (Figure 5.2) record the existence of a basin that developed adjacent to an active island arc complex. The South Mayo Trough comprises a thick succession of Ordovician (Tremadoc to Llanvirn) calc-alkaline volcanics and volcaniclastic sediments, turbidites, andesites and rhyolite tuff bands. Conglomeratic units contain clasts of mafic, intermediate and acid volcanics, quartzites, granites, gneisses, gabbros and low-grade schists. As with the Ballantrae Complex, the sediments record a progressive shallowing from deep-water turbidites to fluvial and deltaic sediments. A significant change in the composition of the detritus, with the incoming of mafic and ultramafic (ophiolitic) clasts and detrital garnet and staurolite, occurs in rocks of early Llanvirn age (c. 470–467 Ma). The northerly-derived ophiolitic and metamorphic detritus can be explained if sedimentation at this time followed erosion of rocks produced by ophiolite obduction and metamorphism associated with the Grampian phase (Figure 5.1c).

5.2.3 Evidence for an ancient subduction zone: the Clew Bay Complex

The Clew Bay Complex exposed in north-west Ireland (Figure 5.2) comprises three fault-bounded units. The northernmost unit comprises low-grade metasediments with mafic volcanics that contain blueschists (the product of low-temperature, high-pressure metamorphism; see Box 2.1) and is interpreted as an accretionary prism. A second unit further south contains serpentinized peridotites, amphibolites, gabbros, a sheeted dyke complex and metapelites, and is interpreted as a deformed ophiolite. A third unit consists of pillow basalts, shales and grits. The occurrence of blueschist-facies assemblages in metamorphosed volcanic rocks is of particular importance as they are indicative of metamorphism in a subduction zone.

5.2.4 Summary of Section 5.2

- A chain of ophiolite fragments and related rocks of oceanic affinity identifies a Grampian suture zone that is located along the line of the present Highland Boundary Fault – Fair Head–Clew Bay Line. This boundary marks the southern margin of Laurentia.

- The ophiolite fragments, the remnants of island arc complexes and blueschists point to the existence of an ancient ocean, within which a southwards-dipping intra-oceanic subduction zone developed.

- Plate convergence led to closure of an oceanic tract(s) and eventually to the intra-oceanic subduction zone and magmatic arcs colliding with the Laurentian margin (Figure 5.1). This collision is referred to as the Grampian phase of the Caledonian Orogeny.

- The timing of the collision and ophiolite obduction, albeit only based on data from one of the ophiolites (Ballantrae), is estimated as c. 478 Ma.

- Collision and obduction of ophiolites by thrusting led to crustal thickening, deformation, metamorphism and magmatism on the Laurentian margin.

5.3 Structural development of the Grampian Highlands

5.3.1 Introduction

In the previous Section, we saw that the Grampian phase resulted from the collision between the Laurentian margin and an intra-oceanic subduction zone and magmatic arc complex. In this Section we will investigate the effects of this collision on the rocks of the Laurentian margin, primarily those exposed in the Grampian Highlands, where the most complete record of the effects of this collision is preserved. The nature of the deformation that occurred as a result of the collision is often visually dramatic (Figure 5.6) and reveals much about how the crust responded to crustal shortening .

Figure 5.6   Folds formed in sediments of the Dalradian Supergroup, Grampian Highlands, as a result of deformation during the Grampian phase.

5.3.2   Structure of the Grampian Highlands

Although in detail the tectonics of the Grampian Highlands is complex, there is a large-scale coherence to the pattern of deformation in that the main structures trend NE–SW across the region and can be traced for hundreds of kilometres along strike. The geometry of the structures is illustrated on the 3-D block diagram of the Grampian Highlands from the Great Glen Fault to the Highland Boundary Fault (Figure. 5.7). This and the following Section describe the geometry of the main structures and the sequence of deformation events responsible for their formation. In areas where a sequence of deformational events has taken place it becomes convenient to label them using a simple code or shorthand, explained in Box 5.1.

Box 5.1 Tectonic shorthand

When we begin to analyse the tectonic structures found in complexly deformed areas, we soon recognize evidence for a sequence of events. Geologists have developed a shorthand notation for the description of these sequences, based on letters to identify the class of structure and a numerical subscript to indicate its position in the order of events. The structures that are usually labelled in this way are folds (F), planar fabrics (S) and linear fabrics (L). In addition, the events themselves are often labelled using D for a deformation event and M for a metamorphic event. So, the first deformation would be labelled D_1. During D_1, any folds that form would be called F_1. If these F_1 folds show an axial plane cleavage, this would be termed S_1, and so on.

It is important to realize that all three classes of structure (F, S and L) *can* form during a single deformation event. However, there is no certainty that they *will* form and even if they did, we may not find evidence for them.

Nonetheless, a place would be reserved for them in any table relating structures to events. The consequence of this is that when geologists talk of an S_2 fabric they are not necessarily implying that they have found an earlier fabric that could be called S_1. What is certain is that they have found some structure, but not necessarily a planar fabric, which can be seen to pre-date the S_2 fabric, and which therefore establishes the existence of an earlier deformation event. For example, a geologist may have seen the S_2 fabric cutting across an earlier fold which would thus have to be designated F_1.

However, this rule does not apply to metamorphic events. Although deformation and metamorphism commonly occur together, this is not always the case. A metamorphic event may occur independently of deformation and the most useful statements are of the form, 'M_1 reached its peak between D_1 and D_2'.

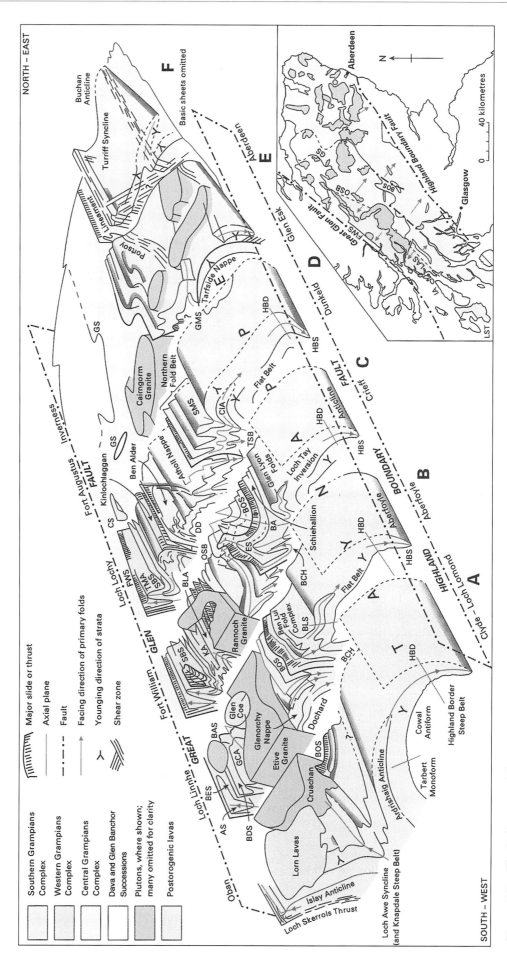

Figure 5.7   Block diagram of the major structures in the Grampian Highlands. The area is divided into the Southern Grampians, Western Grampians and Central Grampians Complexes on the basis of geographical and structural criteria. This diagram is reproduced from one of the standard reference works on Highland geology – Stephenson, D. and Gould, D. (eds) (1995) *The Grampian Highlands*, 4th edn, HMSO for the British Geological Survey.

Key to Figure 5.7

AS	Appin Syncline	GCA	Glen Creran Anticline
BA	Bohespic Antiform	GMS	Glen Mark Slide
BAS	Ballachulish Slide	GS	Grampian Slide
BCH	Beinn a Chuallich Folds	HBD	Highland Border Downbend
BDS	Beinn Don Syncline	HBS	Highland Border Steep Belt
BES	Benderloch Slide	IA	Islay Anticline
BLA	Beinn na Lap Antiform	KA	Kinlochleven Anticline
BLS	Ben Lawers Synform	LAS	Loch Awe Syncline
BOS	Boundary Slide	LST	Loch Skerrols Thrust
CIA	Creag na h'Iolaire Anticline	OSB	Ossian–Geal Charn Steep Belt
CS	Corrieyairick Syncline	SBS	Stob Ban Synform
DD	Drumochter Dome	SMS	Sron Mhor Synform
ES	Errochty Synform	TMA	Tom Meadhoin Anticline
FWS	Fort William Slide	TSB	Tummel Steep Belt

Figure 5.7 shows that the Dalradian and older rocks were deformed into a complex pattern of NE–SW-trending tight to isoclinal folds. The intensity and complexity of deformation increases from the south-west (block A) towards the central region (blocks C and D). Because the structure in block A is relatively simple, this south-western region makes a good introduction to the overall structure of the Highlands. The lavas and intrusions that post-date deformation can be ignored for the moment; the structures of interest are characterized by tectonic contacts and the shapes of folds.

A particularly useful concept that structural geologists apply to understand the structure in areas of complexly deformed rocks is that of fold facing, explained in Box 5.2. Block A in Figure 5.7 shows that in the south-west of the Highlands, the Dalradian rocks have been deformed into a series of folds that form a fan or fountain-like structure with folds facing to the NW and SE, away from a central zone of upright structures. In the north-west, the Islay Anticline faces NW, whereas in the south-east, the Ardrishaig Anticline faces to the SE. In the central area, the rocks are folded about the Loch Awe Syncline. If we trace these structures towards the north-east, the open upright folds typical of the south-west, e.g. the Loch Awe Syncline (block A), decrease in wavelength and their interlimb angles become progressively tighter, forming upright tight to isoclinal folds. The effect of this increase in the intensity of folding is to produce zones of steeply-dipping structures called steep belts, e.g. the Ossian–Geal Charn Steep Belt and the Tummel Steep Belt (OSB and TSB in Figure 5.7, blocks C and D).

Block A shows two other important aspects of the structure:

* In the south-east part of block A, the Ardrishaig Anticline has been overturned towards the south-east, forming a major tight to isoclinal recumbent fold known as the Tay Nappe. The rocks on the lower limb of this fold have been inverted and are therefore upside-down. This nappe is of regional significance and can be traced towards the north-east across the entire region (blocks B to E). Towards the Highland Boundary Fault the rocks of the Tay Nappe have a shallow to sub-horizontal attitude, so this belt of rocks is known as the Flat Belt. Adjacent to the Highland Boundary Fault the Flat Belt rocks of the Tay Nappe are downturned about a line of inflection, called the Highland Border Downbend, into the Highland Border Steep Belt.

- In the north-west part of block A, the lower limb of the Islay Anticline is attenuated (smeared out) along a major zone of dislocation – the Loch Skerrols Thrust. Similarly, a series of thrusts or ductile shear zones are located along the limbs of the major folds across the region, these zones of intense deformation are locally referred to as slides (e.g. the Fort William Slide, FWS and the Boundary Slide, BOS). These structures are thought to be a series of ductile thrusts that developed at the same time as the large-scale NW-facing folds. Slides may be associated with attenuated or missing stratigraphy, and some geologists interpret this as evidence that slides are tectonically reactivated normal faults or unconformities.

Box 5.2 Unravelling multiple events in deformed rocks: the concept of fold facing

Study the folds in Figure 5.8a, where a series of beds with their way-up indicated have been deformed into a simple fold pair. The way-up, or direction of younging, of the beds has been established from the analysis of primary sedimentary structures, such as graded bedding. The conventional symbol used to indicate the direction of younging looks like a capital letter 'Y' but oriented such that the single bar points to the younger beds. The fold on the left closes upwards, so by definition is an antiform. The beds are oldest in the core of the fold, so it can also be described as an anticline. Similarly, the fold on the right is a syncline. Using this terminology to describe the folds in Figure 5.8b we arrive at a confusing terminology in which the fold on the left can be described as an antiformal syncline, and the fold on the right as a synformal anticline. A simpler way of describing folds is to use the concept of

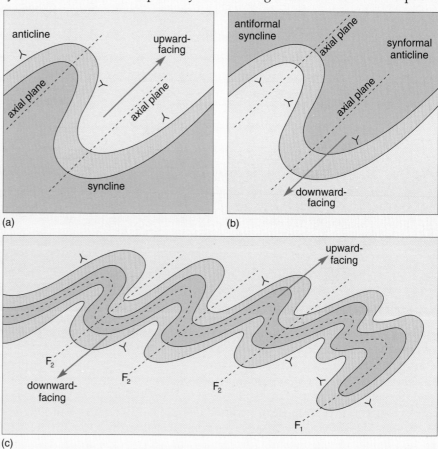

Figure 5.8   The concept of fold facing illustrated by (a) upward-facing folds, (b) downward-facing folds, and (c) a fold structure produced by an early folding episode (with axis labelled F_1) that has been folded in a later episode (axes labelled F_2).

fold facing. Facing is described as the direction, traced along the axial plane of a fold, in which we encounter the younger beds. Using this concept, the folds in Figure 5.8a and b are simply described as upward- and downward-facing, respectively.

This concept becomes extremely useful in complexly deformed areas. In orogenic belts it is not always possible, owing to the scale of structures, to identify fold closures, hence determining the facing direction becomes more important. Why? If you were to unravel the folds in Figure 5.8b you would see that the beds remain upside down. This observation has two important consequences. Firstly, it must indicate that the beds were subjected to an earlier folding event, as only deformation can invert strata. Secondly, the concept of fold facing can be used to identify on which limb of a major fold you may be located. This concept is illustrated in Figure 5.8c where the axial plane of an F_1 fold can be identified by using the concept of facing on the lower and upper limbs. The beds on the lower limb have been inverted by F_1 prior to the formation of F_2 folds. It is this important concept that has enabled geologists to interpret the complex structure of the Grampian Highlands in terms of a fairly simple sequence of folding events, some of which involved the overturning of the Dalradian sedimentary succession.

5.3.3 The deformation sequence

The structure of the Grampian Highlands results from the successive effects of a series of deformations. At least four major phases of deformation (designated D_1 to D_4) that are of regional significance are recognized. A simplified sequence showing the development of these structures is presented in Figure 5.9.

Figure 5.9 A simplified schematic representation of the structural development of the Grampian Highlands, showing (a) upright folds produced by D_1, (b) nappe and slide formation during D_2, and (c) Steep Belt formation during D_3 and D_4.

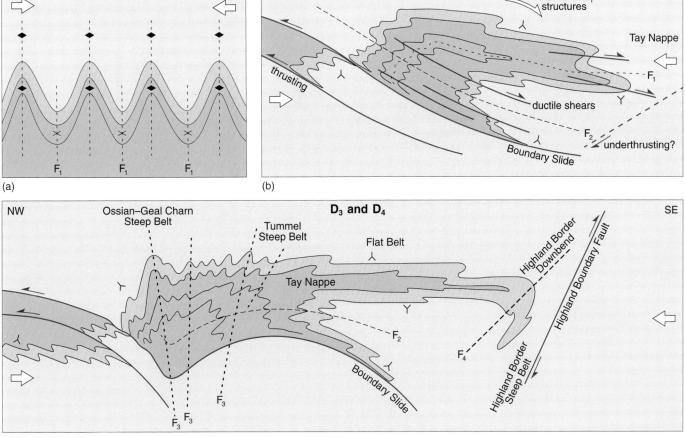

The structures and fabrics formed during the earlier deformations (D_1 and D_2) pervade the rocks and are preserved throughout the region. Evidence for the later deformations (D_3 and D_4), although widespread, is not observed in all areas.

The earliest structures (and associated fabrics) produced as a result of the initial crustal shortening are a set of large-scale synclines and anticlines (F_1), with wavelengths of up to tens of kilometres, e.g. the Ardrishaig Anticline, Loch Awe Syncline and Islay Anticline (Figure 5.7 block A and Figure 5.9a). The original attitude of these folds has proved difficult to assess as a result of the intensity of later deformations, but the general consensus is that they formed a set of open upright folds (Figure 5.9a). The formation of some of these early folds was also partly controlled by the pre-deformation architecture of the Dalradian rift basins. The fault-bounded rift margins and intrabasinal highs that formed during the development of the Dalradian basin (as illustrated in Figure 4.4c) acted as buttresses or rigid blocks against which the sediments were deformed into a series of upright tight to isoclinal folds (Figure 5.10).

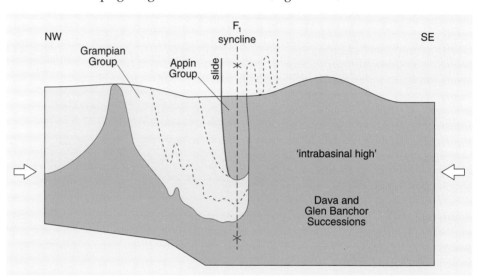

Figure 5.10 Section across the Ossian–Geal Charn Steep Belt showing the formation of early upright folds adjacent to an intrabasinal high. The intrabasinal high acted as a rigid block during compression.

Continued crustal shortening (D_2) led to the formation of ductile fold nappes (F_2). These folds are mainly recumbent to low-angle and tight to isoclinal in style. A series of ductile thrusts or shear zones is associated with the formation of these folds (e.g. the Fort William Slide and the Boundary Slide). The shear zones are primarily located along the attenuated lower limbs of NW-facing folds (Figure 5.9b). Displacements of up to tens of kilometres towards the north-west occurred along the thrusts and shear zones. The formation of the Tay Nappe has presented a particularly interesting problem for structural geologists as it faces towards the SE, a direction different to that of the other major folds of D_2 age. It is envisaged that the Tay Nappe formed as a result of the progressive SE rotation of an earlier fold (F_1), a rotation that was in part driven by a combination of continued NW-directed overthrusting and underthrusting at deeper levels in the crust (Figure 5.9b). The D_2 event led to considerable crustal thickening and the deep burial of rocks.

The early structures were subsequently deformed by later, less intense deformations (D_3 and D_4), which produced a set of NE–SW-trending structures, including open upright folds and structural domes (Figure 5.7 and Figure 5.9c). Examples of these structures are the Cowal Antiform (block A), and the Drumochter Dome (block D). The similar orientation of these later structures to earlier D_2 folds suggests that crustal shortening resulted from continued NW–SE-directed compression. The later phases of folding, F_3 and F_4, also led to the

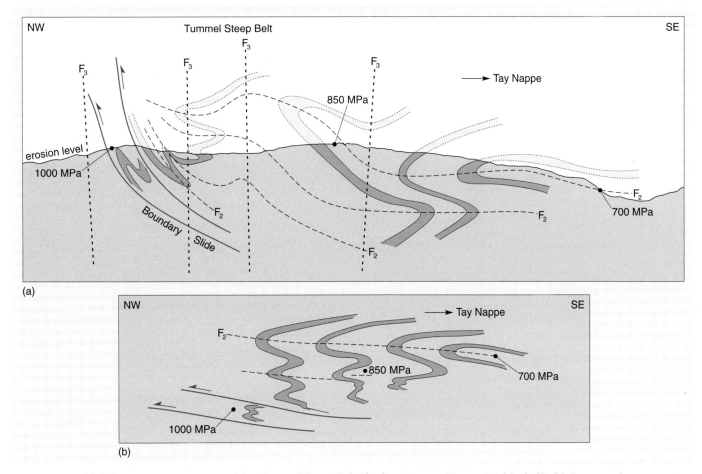

Figure 5.11 (a) Schematic cross-section of the Tummel Steep Belt (for location see Figure 5.7, block C). (b) A restored cross-section of the Tummel Steep Belt illustrating the structural relationships prior to D_3 deformation. Pressure estimates obtained from mineral assemblages record the depths of burial during the D_2 event.

steepening of earlier flat-lying structures (D_2) and the formation of a series of steep belts. D_3 was responsible for the formation of the Tummel Steep Belt (block D) a zone where Flat Belt rocks, comprising D_2 isoclinal folds and shear zones, became steepened in a zone of 10 km of tight upright folding. A simplified cross-section of these structures is illustrated in Figure 5.11.

Removal of the effects of D_3 (Figure 5.11b) shows that the D_2 event, characterized by recumbent folding and thrusting, was associated with burial and thickening of the crust. The higher pressures recorded at progressively deeper structural levels must have resulted from greater burial depth.

Late D_4 deformation results in broad upright folds and formation of the Highland Border Downbend. These structures are responsible for the downturning of the nose of the Tay Nappe along the Highland Border Downbend into the Highland Border Steep Belt (Figures 5.7 and 5.9c).

5.3.4 Summary of Section 5.3

- Deformation, associated with the Grampian collision between Laurentia and an island arc complex, resulted in a complicated sequence of folds and associated structures that can be traced across the Grampian Highlands.

- The early deformations, D_1 and D_2, produced regional scale, recumbent fold nappes, such as the Tay Nappe, and associated thrusts. The pre-deformation architecture of the Dalradian basin (e.g. intrabasinal highs) may have in part controlled the style of deformation. D_1 and D_2 caused considerable tectonic burial of the Dalradian sediments.

- Later deformations (D_3 and D_4) produced upright structures that refolded the earlier nappes, a process that led to the formation of complex fold patterns (e.g. structural domes) and a series of zones of steeply inclined rocks called Steep Belts.

5.4   Metamorphism in the Grampian Highlands

5.4.1   Introduction

In the previous Section we saw that the rocks of the Grampian Highlands were strongly deformed as a result of the collision between Laurentia and an island arc complex. Crustal shortening led to the formation of large-scale folds and thrusts (D_2), a process that ultimately led to their burial. In this Section we will attempt to establish the thermal consequences of the burial of rocks by studying the metamorphism of the rocks now exposed in the Grampian Highlands. In particular we will focus on the metamorphic record preserved in the metasediments of the Dalradian Supergroup. The study of these rocks is especially useful as they have only experienced a single metamorphic episode, and therefore we do not have the added complication of unravelling the effects of multiple periods of metamorphism. It is also helpful that both the stratigraphy (Section 4) and the structure (Section 5.3) are well known. As a result, the Grampian Highlands is a prime area in which to study the causes of regional metamorphism.

5.4.2   The metamorphic map of the Dalradian

The conditions attained during Grampian metamorphism are illustrated in Figure 5.12 – a metamorphic map of the Dalradian Supergroup. Figure 5.12 summarizes the general pattern of metamorphic conditions from the south-west to the north-east across the Grampian Highlands. The map has been constructed from a correlation of metamorphic zones, metamorphic facies and P–T estimates obtained from Dalradian rocks (Boxes 2.1 and 5.3). These estimates record the temperatures and pressures achieved at or near the metamorphic peak.

The lack of correlation between temperature and pressure (or depth) must indicate that metamorphism on a regional scale cannot have resulted simply from burial. During burial you might expect that the rocks that have been buried to the greatest depths would show the highest temperatures. The epidote–amphibolite facies rocks in the south-west have been metamorphosed at $c.$ 450 °C and 700–900 MPa. These are the coldest, yet record some of the highest pressures. Rocks from the north-east (the Buchan region) record similar temperatures but at much lower pressures. Obviously other processes or factors were at work, and must have operated on a much smaller scale than that of the orogen. We will consider how to explain these variations in Section 5.4.5.

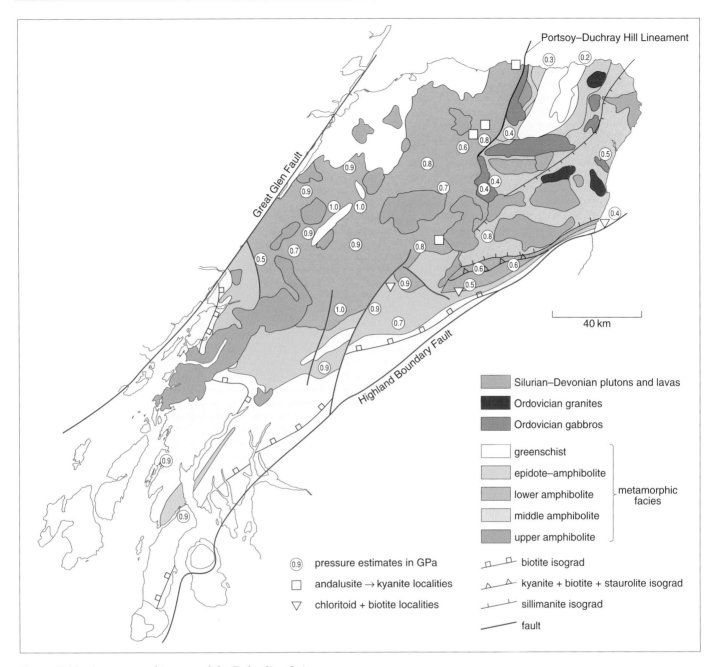

Figure 5.12 A metamorphic map of the Dalradian Supergroup.

On first inspection, Figure 5.12 shows a relatively systematic pressure variation, with pressures decreasing from *c.* 900 MPa in the south-west to 300–400 MPa in the north-east. What might this pattern reflect? It may simply reflect the depth of burial of the rocks, or conversely the amount of uplift and erosion (exhumation) that the more deeply buried rocks have experienced. In this case, the rocks of the south-west and central areas would have been exhumed by a greater extent than those of the north-east. However, the temperatures and pressures associated with the epidote–amphibolite- and lower-amphibolite-facies rocks require a different explanation. The lower-amphibolite-facies rocks (*c.* 550–600 °C) show a range of pressures from 500–1000 MPa. Similarly, epidote–amphibolite-facies rocks (garnet zone) record pressures of 700–900 MPa in the south-west and pressures of 200–400 MPa in the north-east (Buchan area). A simple conclusion from these general observations is that temperatures and pressures of metamorphism across the region are not closely correlated.

Box 5.3 Determining the conditions of metamorphism

Metamorphic rocks show variations in their mineralogy and microstructures that are a function of metamorphic grade. Metamorphic grade is a general term used to describe the intensity of metamorphism. Low grade refers to rocks that have been metamorphosed under conditions of low temperatures and pressures, and are often fine grained, e.g. slates. High-grade rocks have been subjected to higher temperatures and pressures, and are usually coarser grained, e.g. schists and gneisses. Several methods have been developed that allow the metamorphic grade of rocks to be defined more accurately.

The zonal scheme was first established by George Barrow in the south-eastern Scottish Highlands in 1893, where he recognized the progressive change in mineral assemblages in rocks of pelitic composition (mudstones). The boundaries between the zones are defined by isograds, these are lines or surfaces joining rocks of equivalent metamorphic grade. An isograd is defined by the first appearance (not disappearance) of a critical or index mineral, and the zone is named after that mineral, e.g. the garnet isograd marks the start of the garnet zone and is defined by the first occurrence of the mineral garnet. The garnet zone extends to the isograd at which the next index mineral appears (staurolite in this case). Barrow mapped out the regular distribution of the index minerals chlorite–biotite–garnet–staurolite–kyanite–sillimanite and established the sequence of metamorphic zones, which are now known as the Barrovian zones. These zones have subsequently been identified in many orogenic belts world-wide. After Barrow's work, geologists studying the north-east Highlands recognized a different sequence of index minerals and zones: biotite–cordierite–andalusite–sillimanite; these have been called the Buchan zones (Figure 5.13) after the geographical area in which they were found. These zones record the changes in pressure and temperature experienced by the rocks.

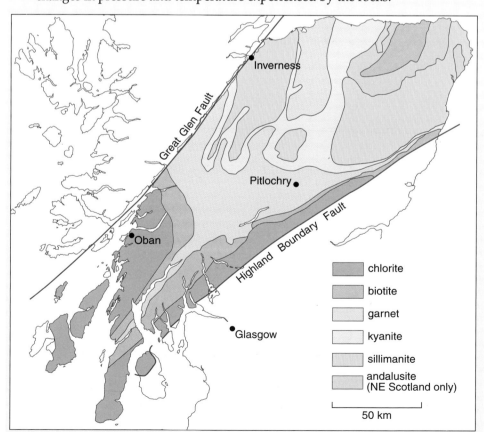

chlorite

biotite

garnet

kyanite

sillimanite

andalusite (NE Scotland only)

50 km

Figure 5.13 The distribution of metamorphic zones in the Grampian Highlands of Scotland. The staurolite zone is a narrow zone between the garnet and kyanite zones, and is not shown.

What does an isograd represent? An isograd identifies the location where the products and reactants of a metamorphic reaction are at equilibrium. The growth of the new mineral, or minerals, that defines the isograd has occurred in response to the change in temperature and pressure. Minerals stable at lower grades are no longer stable under the new higher-grade conditions and as a result break down to form a new mineral, or set of minerals, that is stable under the new conditions. A series of isograds therefore represents a set of metamorphic reactions that occur as a result of increasing pressures and temperatures.

The zonal sequence is useful for describing metamorphism in areas that are dominated by rocks of a single bulk composition, e.g. pelites. Yet in many areas, rocks of pelitic composition may be absent and as a consequence the correlation of grade between areas is difficult. The use of metamorphic facies (Box 2.1), rather than individual index minerals, is then a much more reliable approach to evaluating metamorphic grade.

The zonal and facies schemes provide semi-quantitative information on the metamorphic grade based on the simple description of minerals observed in rocks in the field and/or in hand specimen. Modern geological tools (such as the electron microprobe, which provides chemical analyses of minerals), and apparatus for high-P–T experiments on rocks, together with the application of equilibrium thermodynamics to metamorphic reactions, have allowed the positions on a P–T diagram of metamorphic reactions and the stability fields of key minerals and mineral assemblages to be refined. These studies allow the construction of a P–T diagram showing a set of reactions that a rock of a particular bulk composition may experience during its evolution. Such a diagram is called a P–T or petrogenetic grid. A simple petrogenetic grid appropriate for the metamorphism of Dalradian mudstones is illustrated in Figure 5.14.

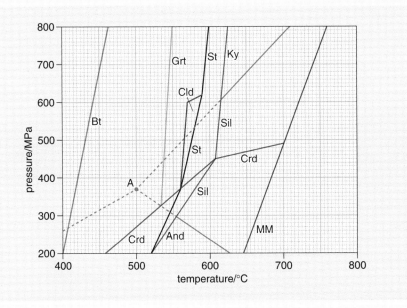

Figure 5.14 A simplified petrogenetic grid appropriate for the metamorphism of Dalradian pelites. The reaction boundaries mark the incoming of the various minerals (indicated) and their stability fields. In the Dalradian, the compositions of the pelites are such that the aluminosilicates only appear to the right of the purple line. To the left of this line, other minerals use up all the available aluminium in the rock. Abbreviations: Bt biotite; Grt garnet; Cld chloritoid; St staurolite; Ky kyanite; Sil sillimanite; And andalusite; Crd cordierite; MM muscovite melting. A = the triple point where andalusite, kyanite and sillimanite can all coexist.

Many of the reactions on the grid have steep slopes, meaning that the stability of the minerals involved is more sensitive to temperature than to pressure. These reactions are termed geothermometers. Reactions that have a relatively flat slope on the P–T diagram are more sensitive to changes in pressure and are termed geobarometers. The use of these methods allows the geologist to locate the pressure and temperature at which a metamorphic assemblage crystallized, usually within a few tens of degrees and a few tens of MPa.

5.4.3 The relative timing of porphyroblast growth and deformation

We saw in Section 5.3 that deformation of the Dalradian Supergroup involved at least four major phases (D_1–D_4). Once the sequence of folding and fabric development has been established in an area, a more detailed study of the relationship between deformation and metamorphism can be attempted. As an example, the sequence of major compressional deformation events that formed the Tay Nappe and Tummel Steep Belt has been established, and is illustrated in Figures 5.9 and 5.11. We can now bring in the results of textural studies of the fabrics and porphyroblasts in pelitic schists from that part of the Highlands (specifically the area near Schiehallion, Figure 5.7, block C). Some of the critical evidence is illustrated in Figure 5.15, and the methods outlined in Box 5.4 lead to the following constraints on the metamorphism and structural evolution of the Highlands during the Grampian phase.

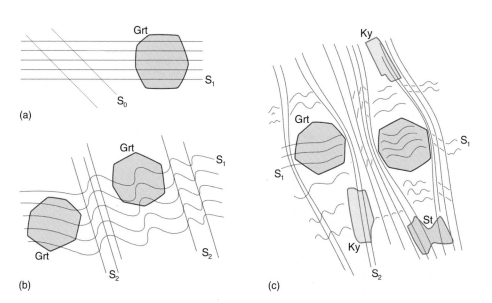

Figure 5.15 The generalized sequence of porphyroblast growth in relation to fabric development from the area around Schiehallion, in the Grampian Highlands. (a) Garnet (Grt) initially overgrows S_0 and S_1. (b) Garnet continues to grow during the early stages of S_2, as indicated by the preservation of microfolds developed during D_2 as inclusion trails in the garnet. (c) The S_2 fabric wraps the garnet, and both staurolite (St) and kyanite (Ky) overprint S_2. Note that remnants of S_1 are only preserved in areas of low strain or as inclusion trails in garnet.

In Figure 5.15, garnet has overprinted both the primary sedimentary layering designated, by convention, S_0 and an early metamorphic fabric S_1, therefore garnet must have started growing after formation of S_1. Elsewhere in the rock garnet is observed overprinting small-scale folds (microfolds) that were formed during a second deformation episode (D_2) (Figure 5.15b). As the intensity of D_2 increased, a further fabric, S_2, developed axial planar to the microfolds (Figure 5.15b) and eventually wrapped the early garnets (Figure 5.15c). These observations would indicate that garnet continued to grow during the early stages of D_2. The analysis of inclusion trails in porphyroblasts of both staurolite and kyanite suggest that they grew after the S_2 fabric had wrapped the garnets, hence they grew after D_2 (Figure 5.15c).

The sequence of porphyroblast mineral growth (the Barrovian index minerals garnet → staurolite → kyanite) suggests that temperatures and pressures increased during and after D_2, believed to have been the main nappe-forming event in the Grampian Highlands. This result is confirmed by the estimates of pressures obtained from three structural levels in the D_2 nappe pile in the vicinity of the D_3 Tummel Steep Belt (Figure 5.11). Detailed studies carried out across the orogen as a whole have established that, in general, peak metamorphic mineral growth occurred after D_2, the nappe-forming event, and in some areas continued during upright folding D_3.

Box 5.4 Textural dating

Metamorphic mineral growth can occur before, during or after a deformation event. To date the timing or sequence of mineral growth in relation to a deformation event, geologists use the textural relationships between the minerals that grew during metamorphism and the microfabrics that developed during deformation to deduce a sequence of events. The most useful minerals to use are porphyroblasts – minerals that have grown much larger than the surrounding finer-grained matrix.

Deformed rocks often exhibit a preferred orientation of certain minerals, usually the platy minerals such as micas, which form linear fabrics (lineations) and planar fabrics (foliations). As these fabrics form as a result of deformation, the minerals that are aligned must have grown during the deformation event, and such minerals are therefore termed syn-kinematic.

Aligned platy minerals, such as micas in schist, and elongate minerals, such as amphiboles in metamorphosed basalt, are examples of syn-kinematic growth. On the other hand, equidimensional porphyroblasts (e.g. garnet) that grew during deformation often show evidence of having been rotated. These syn-kinematic porphyroblasts are often identified by the study of the orientation of small crystals included within the porphyroblast as it grew; these are called inclusion trails. The inclusion trail in the mineral will be continuous with the matrix foliation, but shows progressive deflection into the core of the porphyroblast (Figure 5.16a). The synchronous deformation and crystal growth that leads to S-shaped, spiral or snowball inclusion trails often occurs in shear zones and is sketched in Figure 5.17; Figure 5.18 shows an example.

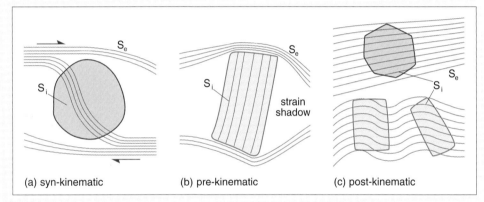

Figure 5.16 Criteria used to establish the relative timing of porphyroblast growth and deformation rely on the relationship between the internal fabric (S_i), represented by inclusion trails in a porphyroblast, to the external fabric (S_e).

(a) syn-kinematic   (b) pre-kinematic   (c) post-kinematic

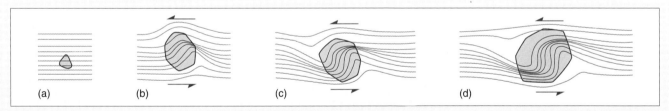

(a)   (b)   (c)   (d)

Figure 5.17   Stages in the growth of a syn-kinematic garnet porphyroblast during progressive sinistral shear deformation.

When porphyroblast growth pre-dates deformation the porphyroblasts will be parallel to, and often wrapped by the fabric; such crystals are termed pre-kinematic. In this case the inclusion trail will be oblique to the foliation and often truncated by it

(Figure 5.16b). These porphyroblasts often show the effect of tectonic strains induced by later deformation by the development of features such as fracturing, kink banding or microfolding, boudinage, undulose extinction and strain shadows (Figures 5.19 and 5.20).

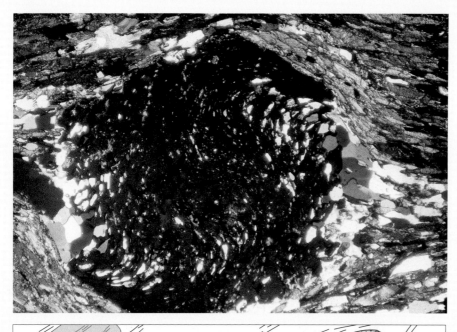

Figure 5.18 Photomicrograph of an S-shaped inclusion trail in a garnet porphyroblast.

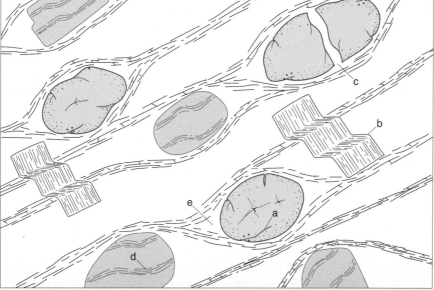

Figure 5.19 Microtextural features indicative of pre-kinematic growth of porphyroblasts: (a) fractures; (b) kink bands; (c) boudinage (pull-apart structures); (d) undulose or strained extinction; (e) strain shadows.

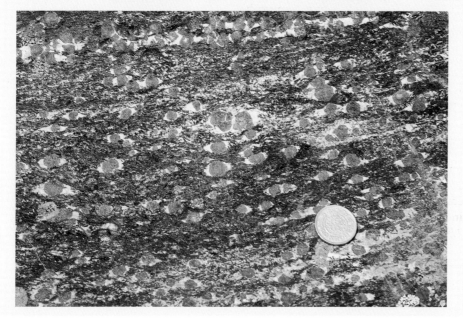

Figure 5.20 Field photograph of pre-kinematic garnet porphyroblasts with strain shadows.

Figure 5.21 Photomicrograph of post-kinematic chloritoid crystals from north-east Greenland.

Porphyroblasts that grow after a deformation event are usually identified by their random orientation and the fact that they overgrow the earlier-formed fabric of the rock; such porphyroblasts are termed post-kinematic. In thin section, any pre-existing fabrics will simply be overprinted and inclusion trails will retain the same form as the fabric in the matrix (Figures 5.16c and 5.21).

In orogenic belts, metamorphic minerals may grow during several phases of deformation. Unravelling the timing of porphyroblast growth relative to a series of deformation-induced fabrics is the key to understanding the connection between metamorphism and deformation. For example, porphyroblasts may overgrow an early fabric and preserve its form as an inclusion trail; the porphyroblast may then become wrapped by a later fabric that formed after the porphyroblast stopped growing. By linking such microstructures and fabrics to events that are of regional significance (e.g. fold phases), the causes of metamorphism may be put into a tectonic context. In addition, radiometric dating of metamorphic mineral growth can help establish a chronological framework for orogenesis.

5.4.4 The absolute timing of metamorphic mineral growth

Radiometric dating of garnet-bearing rocks has provided some important constraints on the timing of metamorphic mineral growth in the Grampian Highlands. As well as it being possible to date the age at which metamorphic garnet grew, it is also possible (using geothermometers; see Box 5.3) to estimate the temperature at which garnet grew. Recently, researchers have started to combine these two techniques to deduce the temperature–time history of Dalradian metasediments during the Grampian phase. They have found that in the garnet zone, the metamorphic peak was reached during D_3 with garnet crystallizing at 500–550 °C; these garnets give an age of 467.6 ± 2.5 Ma. In the sillimanite zone, two episodes of garnet growth are recognized by textural studies. The earlier episode occurred during D_2 at 500–550 °C; these garnets give an age of 472.9 ± 2.9 Ma. At a later time, during D_3, garnets grew alongside sillimanite under higher-grade conditions, estimated as 550–660 °C, and these have an age of 464.8 ± 2.7 Ma. The sillimanite zone therefore shows evidence of having evolved through increasing metamorphic grade over time until reaching a peak at c. 465 Ma. Given the uncertainty in the radiometric ages, the ages of peak conditions in the garnet (467.6 ± 2.5 Ma) and sillimanite (464.8 ± 2.7 Ma) zones are essentially indistinguishable. The metamorphic peak in the intervening zones (staurolite and kyanite) must also have been attained at around the same time, at c. 465–468 Ma.

5.4.5 The causes of Grampian metamorphism

Metamorphic rocks record pressures and temperatures attained during perturbations to the crust's thermal structure caused by orogenesis and igneous intrusions. By comparing observations made on metamorphic rocks from orogenic belts with models that predict how P and T change with time during crustal thickening and exhumation, geologists can learn about large-scale orogenic processes. Such models are outlined in Box 5.5, where it is shown that the normal consequence of crustal thickening by overthrusting is that rocks tectonically buried to progressively greater depths take systematically longer to reach their metamorphic peak. In the Dalradian, however, we have just seen that the metamorphic peak in the different metamorphic zones (i.e. at different crustal levels) was reached nearly simultaneously. This is contrary to the expectation from models of metamorphism resulting from crustal thickening and erosion-controlled exhumation alone. An additional heat source is required during the Grampian phase.

The most obvious source of heat would be that provided by the addition of magma into the crust. If a magmatic heat source was responsible for the necessary additional heat, then several important criteria must be fulfilled. Firstly, there should be a spatial link between magmatism and the highest-grade metamorphic rocks, and the metamorphic grade should increase towards the intrusive bodies. Secondly, the magmas would have to have been emplaced at or near the metamorphic peak. Thirdly, significant volumes of magma would be required in order to generate a large enough thermal response.

On studying the distribution of igneous bodies in Figure 5.12, it is evident that a suite of Ordovician granites and gabbros is located in the north-east of the region (Buchan); these could be of the right age. The larger Silurian granites can be discounted as they are far too young, having been emplaced some considerable time after the metamorphic peak. Note too that the gabbros are spatially linked to the region of high temperatures, as indicated by the distribution of the facies and the location of the sillimanite isograd. But do they fulfil the other criteria?

Studies on the emplacement history of the Ordovician granitic bodies indicate that they were emplaced synchronously with D_3. Radiometric dating on these bodies gives an age of $c.$ 470–467 Ma. One of these bodies, the Aberdeen granite ($c.$ 470 Ma), was emplaced into rocks that were still undergoing high-temperature regional metamorphism and partial melting ($c.$ 500–550 MPa and 700 °C). The structural and absolute age of the granite bodies is synchronous with the ages obtained for the metamorphic peak. Could these intrusions have provided the additional heat source? Given that only three small plutons have been identified at the present exposure level it seems unlikely that they could have been the cause of the regional metamorphism. It is more likely that these granites were an end product (rather than the cause) of high-grade metamorphism during which temperatures were high enough to partially melt the metasediments. Indeed, the high initial $^{87}Sr/^{86}Sr$ ratios (0.7112 and 0.7117) of the granites indicate that they were a product of the melting of Dalradian metasediments.

The Ordovician granites are spatially associated with a suite of gabbroic rocks collectively known as the Newer Gabbros (e.g. the Morven–Cabrach and the Insch gabbros). The gabbros were intruded post-D_2 and syn-D_3 and produced, in places, a sillimanite overprint on the regional metamorphic zones. Their intrusion ages are $c.$ 470 Ma. P–T estimates obtained from rocks metamorphosed in the aureoles of several of these bodies consistently give values of c. 750–850 °C and 400–500 MPa, pressures that equate to depths of between 15–18 km. The gabbros are of greater areal extent than the granites, and an estimate of c. 5.5 km thickness for the Insch gabbro would suggest that they are of considerable mass. The geochemistry and the isotopic composition of the gabbros have provided constraints on their source. In particular the low initial $^{87}Sr/^{86}Sr$ ratio (c. 0.706) obtained on the Newer Gabbros is compatible with an origin by mantle melting in a calc-alkaline arc.

The emplacement of a series of such gabbroic bodies into the crust would have several important consequences. Firstly, the gabbros would provide a significant heat source at mid-crustal levels and enhance the heat flow in the upper crust, as gabbroic magma has a much higher temperature (c. 1100 °C) than granitic magma (c. 700 °C). The near-simultaneous emplacement of these gabbros (over a time span of c. 7 million years) would produce a short-lived thermal spike. Although precise ages are rather limited, such a spike could explain the peak of metamorphism at the same time in several of the metamorphic zones. The additional heat supplied by the gabbros may also have led to partial melting of the metasediments and culminated in the generation and emplacement of the Ordovician granites. The high heat flow generated would also promote high geothermal gradients typical of Buchan-type metamorphism. Secondly, the addition of several c. 5.5 km thick bodies would cause significant crustal thickening. In an area where the rocks below the gabbros are seen, there is evidence for the transformation of andalusite to kyanite – a transformation that requires an increase in pressure (Figure 5.14), so this observation gives support to the idea that gabbro intrusion caused major perturbations in pressure and temperature.

Box 5.5 Geotherms, P–T–t paths and orogeny

Our understanding of the thermal history of mountain belts has been greatly enhanced by the application of models that predict the effects of orogeny on the thermal structure of the lithosphere.

The variation of temperature with depth in the lithosphere is called the geotherm. In continental crust, it is mainly controlled by heat flowing upwards from the mantle into the lower crust and by heat produced by radioactive decay of K, Th and U isotopes in the upper crust. The heat is principally transferred by conduction. In regions of long-term tectonic stability, the geotherm remains constant over time and is therefore called a steady-state geotherm.

The steady-state geotherm will only change as a result of a change in the thickness of the crust caused by orogeny, or by the intrusion of magma. Changing the geothermal gradient by conduction is a slow process as rocks are good insulators (they have low values of thermal conductivity) and are slow to conduct heat. As a result, there is a time lag between a disturbance or perturbation of the crust and the establishment of a new steady-state geotherm. This slow change is called thermal relaxation. Any geotherm that exists during this period is called a transient geotherm. For a transient geotherm to relax to a steady-state geotherm can take tens of millions of years. As tectonic events such as thrusting and thickening take less time, the geotherm may not reach a steady state until some considerable time after the perturbation event. As a result the thermal state of the lithosphere will be continually changing during orogeny.

Let us take a simple example where the crust is thickened by the overthrusting of another 30 km thick crustal block and then thinned back to its normal thickness by erosion of the surface (Figure 5.22).

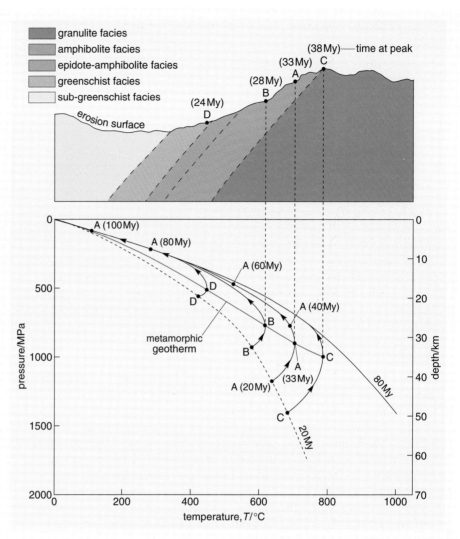

Figure 5.22 Evolution of individual rocks (A to D) in *P–T* space during a single cycle of orogenesis involving burial and exhumation. The diagram also illustrates the concept of a metamorphic geotherm. The various rocks A–D exposed at the surface have recorded their maximum temperatures at different times, so a metamorphic geotherm cannot represent a geothermal gradient that existed at one time in the evolution of the orogen. The times in brackets on the erosion surface indicate the time after burial at which each sample reached its metamorphic peak.

Consider the evolution of rock A. The development of *P–T* conditions through which rock A has passed at 20, 33, 40, 60, 80 and 100 million years (My) after its rapid burial is shown. At the time immediately after overthrusting, the rock will be at its maximum burial depth or pressure. At 20 My after burial the rock lies on a transient geotherm. The transient geotherm will be low (i.e. relatively low temperature for a given depth, relative to a steady-state geotherm) as a result of the slow rate of thermal relaxation. In time the rock will heat up. The mechanical response of the crust to this period of overthickening will be a period of isostatic uplift. Rocks at the surface will undergo erosion, and all the rocks in the pile will rise to higher structural levels and lower pressures. Rock A will continue to heat up as long as heat production in the crust is greater than the heat loss by conduction to the overlying (and surrounding) rocks. For rock A, pressure gradually decreases but temperature continues to rise, reaching a maximum after 33 My. At this point, heat production balances heat loss by conduction. Thereafter, loss of heat by conduction outweighs the heat production, and rock A begins to cool. At shallower levels in the crust even greater heat is lost by conduction to the surface. After 80 My the rock merges with the steady-state geotherm and finally reaches the surface after 115 My. As a result, rock A describes a *P–T–t* (pressure–temperature–time) loop or path characteristic of its position in the rock pile. The evolution of three other rocks that started at different depths in the pile is also shown in Figure 5.22.

Although this is a simple example, several important points emerge.

- The metamorphic geotherm (the red line joining the maximum temperatures reached by rocks A, B, C and D in Figure 5.22) is not a true geotherm because it does not record the conditions that occurred in the crust at any one time in the past.

- Rocks buried to greater depth take longer to reach their maximum temperatures and they reach the surface later.

- The P–T–t paths followed by rocks that have evolved as a result of crustal thickening show temperatures increasing then decreasing with falling pressure.

- Each rock in the pile preserves its own P–T–t path, and the rocks that reached the higher grades may not always pass through the same P–T points as those of lower grades.

Consequently, the study of the thermal evolution of a metamorphic belt relies on the detailed study of the P–T–t paths recorded by the assemblages in individual samples, and not from integrating the results from a set of samples.

5.4.6 A synthesis of Grampian metamorphism

Variations in the pattern of metamorphism across the Grampian Highlands indicate that metamorphism cannot be ascribed to any one simple event. Although broadly compatible with models of a single cycle of crustal thickening, heating and erosion, variations on a scale much smaller than the orogen as a whole indicate that additional processes were involved. In the south-west, an area we have commented on briefly, the low temperatures characteristic of this region are thought to have resulted from the metamorphism of crust of low thermal conductivity. In the central region, typical Barrovian-type (medium-pressure) metamorphism requires an additional heat supply. In the north-east, in the Buchan-type area (high temperature, medium and low pressure), high-geothermal gradients are attributed to deep-seated intrusions. In addition, the transformation of andalusite (low P) to kyanite (high P) is incompatible with the shape of typical P–T–t paths predicted by models of simple orogenic crustal thickening (Figure 5.22) and may therefore have resulted from a different thickening process (such as gabbro intrusion) that operated on a local scale.

5.4.7 Summary of Section 5.4

- The distribution of temperature and pressure across the Dalradian outcrop indicates that crustal thickening alone could not have been entirely responsible for the metamorphism; metamorphism was not simply a consequence of tectonic burial.

- The relative timing of porphyroblast growth indicates that the metamorphic peak occurred after D_2 (the nappe-forming event) and continued during D_3, an observation that is consistent across the region.

- Geochronology indicates that the peak of metamorphism occurred at c. 470–465 Ma.

- The metamorphic peak was coeval with the emplacement of a suite of granitic and gabbroic magmas. The gabbroic magmas may have provided an additional heat source for metamorphism, in addition to that generated in response to crustal thickening.

5.5   Summary of Section 5

- The Grampian phase of the Caledonian Orogeny resulted from the collision of an intra-oceanic subduction zone and island arc complex with Laurentia (Figure 5.1). The collision led to the obduction of ophiolites and to deformation, metamorphism and magmatism on the Laurentian margin.

- During collision, crustal shortening was accommodated by the formation of regional-scale recumbent fold nappes, thrusts and later upright folds – a process that led to the burial of rocks and to regional metamorphism.

- Studies of the metamorphic rocks now exposed in the Grampian Highlands reveal that crustal thickening alone was not the entire cause of the regional metamorphism. A combination of studies involving theoretical thermal modelling, precise radiometric dating (on both metamorphic minerals and intrusive magmatic rocks) and the distribution of pressure and temperature in the Dalradian rocks points to metamorphism being enhanced by the intrusion of large volumes of gabbroic magma into the crust.

6 Exhumation of the Grampian mountains

6.1 Introduction

Section 5 discussed the collision of an island arc with the margin of Laurentia, which led to the formation of a major mountain belt, the Grampian mountains, to the north of the Highland Boundary Fault – Fair Head–Clew Bay Line. Sections 5.3 and 5.4 concentrated primarily on the crustal thickening processes that were induced by the collision and led to deformation and metamorphism of the Dalradian Supergroup. After a major phase of crustal thickening the crust is mechanically unstable. Erosion also causes isostatic readjustments that lead to the uplift and erosion of the deeply buried rocks. Section 5.4.5 established that rocks of the Dalradian Supergroup were tectonically buried to a variety of depths, as indicated by the range of pressure estimates (c. 200–1000 MPa) obtained from rocks outcropping across the Grampian Highlands. Looking at this in another way, these pressure estimates identify the extent of uplift and erosion, or exhumation, and indicate the amount of overburden that has been removed from various parts of the belt. This Section investigates the exhumation of the deeply buried rocks. Section 6.2 looks at the uplift and cooling history of the metamorphosed Dalradian rocks that are exposed in the Grampian Highlands. In addition, Section 6.3 describes a suite of post-kinematic granites and examines how their generation and intrusion may have been related to exhumation. Section 6.4 investigates how provenance studies can help to determine the source and timing of sediment dispersal into the surrounding basins. Section 6.5 summarizes the nature and time span of the Grampian mountain-building phase.

6.2 Uplift and cooling history of the Grampian mountains

One constraint on the timing of exhumation comes from determining the uplift and cooling history of the metamorphosed Dalradian rocks by dating different metamorphic minerals. As explained in Box 6.1, the radiometric ages of metamorphic minerals define the times at which they cooled through particular temperatures, so they can be used to indicate when deeply buried rocks were exhumed and uplifted towards the surface. One such set of results from the south-eastern Highlands is shown in Figure 6.1, and illustrates that metamorphic biotites began to cool through their closure temperature at c. 473 Ma. Interestingly, this was shortly after the obduction of the Ballantrae ophiolite (dated at c. 478 Ma; Section 5.2.1). Whereas the high-grade rocks started passing through their closure temperatures at c. 470 Ma, the more southerly, lower-grade, rocks cooled much later (c. 410–400 Ma). Similar results have been established from the application of K–Ar and Rb–Sr methods to biotite and muscovite micas from across the orogen. These data suggest that the exhumation of rocks metamorphosed during the Grampian phase was in the Ordovician and occurred almost immediately after the peak of metamorphism (c. 470–465 Ma).

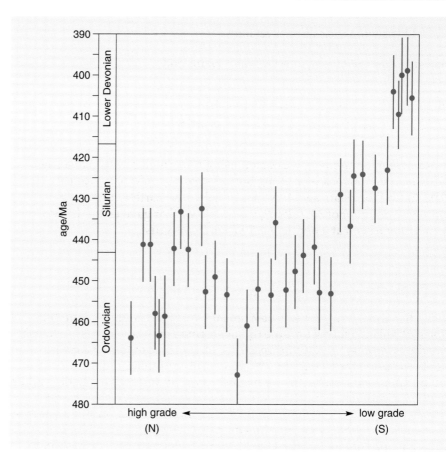

Figure 6.1   The cooling ages of Dalradian biotites (K–Ar method) from N–S traverses across metamorphic zones in the south-eastern Highlands. The cooling ages can be seen to decrease with decreasing metamorphic grade (grade decreases southwards, towards the Highland Boundary Fault, see for example Figures 5.12 and 5.13).

Box 6.1 Determining metamorphic cooling ages using Rb–Sr and K–Ar isotope data

The radioactive decay of parent isotopes (e.g. ^{87}Rb, ^{40}K) to produce daughter isotopes (in this case ^{87}Sr, ^{40}Ar) provides geochronometers that are used to date minerals according to the amount of daughter isotope that has accumulated.

Above a certain temperature, however, isotopes can diffuse into or out of minerals, so the 'radiometric clock' only starts to operate once the mineral has fallen below the temperature at which the mineral becomes a closed system – the closure temperature. Geochronological information is frozen into the mineral as it cools through the closure temperature, hence the radiometric age obtained can be referred to as the cooling age.

In single cycle orogens, that is orogens that have only experienced a single heating or orogenic event, it is possible to take advantage of radiometric isotopes in minerals that have not been reset by subsequent heating events to establish the timing of events during the later part of orogenic development, when the rocks of the orogen are cooling and uplifting.

Each geochronological method records slightly different information about the exhumation history of a rock. This is because different minerals have different closure temperatures, as the examples in Table 6.1 illustrate. So, if a rock contains hornblende, biotite and muscovite, then we can use these minerals to tell us the times at which the rock was at different levels in the crust.

Table 6.1 Examples of closure temperatures.

Parent–daughter system	Biotite	Muscovite	Hornblende
K–Ar	300 °C	320 °C	525 °C
Rb–Sr	uncertain	550 °C	uncertain

For example if a muscovite was dated using K–Ar methods to give an age of 400 Ma, then the rock containing the muscovite would have been at 320 °C 400 million years ago. If we assume that the Earth's crust has a geothermal gradient of 30 °C km^{-1}, then the rock that gave us the 400 Ma age must have been at a depth of *c.* 10.7 km in the crust.

6.3 Magmatism during exhumation

Following the Grampian phase, post-kinematic magmatism throughout the Grampian Highlands formed a suite of undeformed granites and lavas. To help identify the magma generation processes and the source of these magmas, geologists looked at the initial ^{87}Sr/^{86}Sr ratios of the granites (Figure 6.2). Two groups are apparent from the Sr isotope data: a group with relatively high ratios (0.712–0.733), which suddenly give way, at *c.* 435 Ma, to a group with lower ratios (0.704–0.708). The young, low ^{87}Sr/^{86}Sr, group will be discussed in Section 8.7, but here the *c.* 460–435 Ma post-kinematic granites (located in Figure 6.3) are of interest because of the timing of their emplacement and the similarity of their isotope ratios to those of the syn-metamorphic, syn-kinematic granites. The high initial ^{87}Sr/^{86}Sr ratios of the granites indicate that they were most likely to have

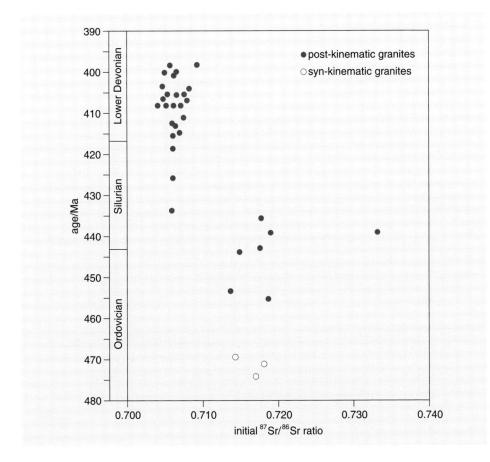

Figure 6.2 Ages and initial ^{87}Sr/^{86}Sr ratios of syn- and post-kinematic granites and lavas from the Grampian Highlands.

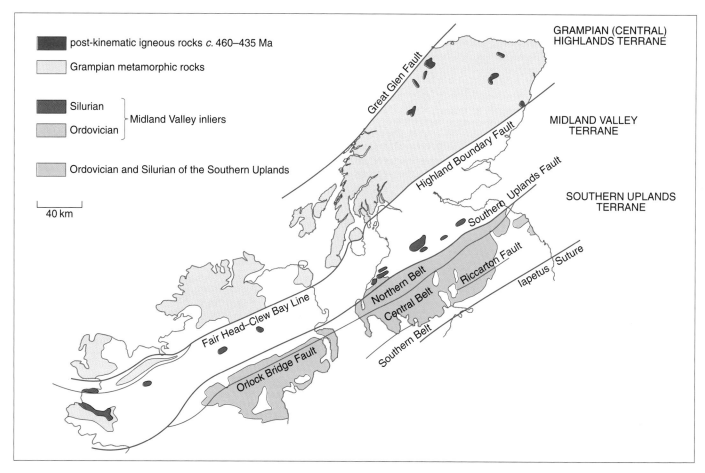

Figure 6.3 Map showing the location of Ordovician and Silurian igneous and sedimentary rocks.

been derived from the partial melting of Dalradian metasediments. The age of the high $^{87}Sr/^{86}Sr$ post-kinematic granites overlaps with the time during which the high-grade metamorphic rocks of the Dalradian Supergroup were uplifting and cooling, so we are led to ask a simple question: how can granite magmas be generated from metasediments during uplift and erosion of a mountain belt?

A reaction that can produce granitic magmas by the melting of metasedimentary rocks is:

muscovite + quartz + plagioclase = granite melt + Al_2SiO_5 + alkali feldspar

The approximate slope and location of this reaction in P–T space is illustrated in Figure 5.14 (reaction labelled MM). It has a positive slope on the P–T diagram, and a granitic melt is generated on the high-temperature, low-pressure side.

● What would be the consequences of a near-isothermal decompression P–T–t path, the result of substantial uplift and erosion, on a rock that had been (tectonically) buried to 700 MPa and 700 °C?

● Decompression of at least 200 MPa (representing 6 km of erosion) at 700 °C crosses the melting reaction, implying the partial melting of the metasediments and the formation of migmatites. During uplift the melts will segregate or separate from their source rocks and ascend through the crust, eventually crystallizing as larger plutonic granite bodies at shallower crustal levels.

The c. 460–435 Ma post-kinematic granites may have been generated in this way during exhumation.

6.4   The record of exhumation in sedimentary basins

We have already seen in Sections 2, 3 and 4 how the composition and age of detrital minerals and rock fragments can be used to establish the provenance of sediments and in some cases identify the nature of missing source terranes. Garnet is a useful indicator of provenance because it can withstand transport in fluvial and deltaic environments, it is resistant to chemical modification and low-grade metamorphism, and its chemical composition can be specific to its source region. Capitalizing on this last point, the record of an orogen's exhumation may be read in a sedimentary succession from an adjacent basin by matching the chemical compositions of detrital garnets to the compositions of garnets in the sedimentary source region. The results of a study of the composition of detrital garnets extracted from sediments deposited in the Midland Valley and Southern Uplands Terranes are shown in Figure 6.4. Also shown in this figure are the compositional ranges or fields of garnets from various potential source rocks.

The composition of detrital garnets in *c.* 465–460 Ma (mid-Llanvirn) sediments that overlie the Ballantrae Complex of the Midland Valley (Figure 6.4a) plot within the compositional field of garnets from the Barrovian zones of the Dalradian. These data suggest that the neighbouring Grampian mountains were eroding and supplying sediment into the Midland Valley as early as *c.* 465 Ma. Of additional interest is that some garnets have compositions identical to those from blueschist-facies rocks; the source of these rare garnets is unclear, but they may have been sourced from a nearby subduction zone.

Figure 6.4b shows the compositions of detrital garnets from sediments of *c.* 457 Ma (early Caradoc) and *c.* 450 Ma (late Caradoc) from the Southern Uplands Terrane. Several important points emerge from the figure. Firstly, the samples contain a few eclogite- and blueschist-facies garnets from the subduction zone complexes. Secondly, the majority of garnets are from a Barrovian source, but interestingly, the earlier garnets have compositions similar to low-grade garnet whereas the younger garnets include compositions that are

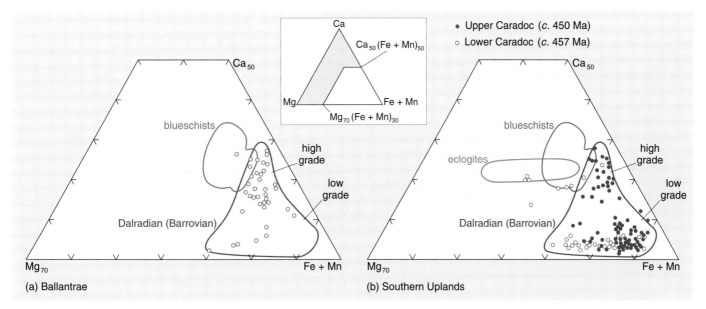

Figure 6.4   The composition of garnets from various sources shown on Ca–Mg–(Fe+Mn) discrimination diagrams. The compositional ranges of garnet from blueschists, eclogites and Dalradian metasediments are indicated. (a) The composition of detrital garnets from the *c.* 465–460 Ma sediments overlying the Ballantrae Complex of the Midland Valley. (b) The composition of detrital garnets from *c.* 457 Ma and *c.* 450 Ma sediments from the Southern Uplands. The inset shows the location of the plots on the full Ca–Mg–(Fe+Mn) diagram.

more typical of higher-grade compositions. An interpretation of this trend is that it represents a simple unroofing sequence: first low-grade then high-grade garnets were exhumed. Thus by the end of the Caradoc (c. 450 Ma) the Southern Uplands Terrane was receiving detritus from the roots of the adjacent Grampian mountains and an associated subduction complex.

The data from the detrital garnet studies indicate that the Grampian Highlands were undergoing significant uplift and erosion and providing metamorphic detritus that was being dispersed southwards by c. 465 Ma. Uplift and erosion must have occurred rapidly after the peak of metamorphism, as the detritus is nearly the same age as the sediment in which it lies. In other words, the metamorphic and igneous rocks from the roots of the Grampian mountains had crystallized, cooled, exhumed, eroded and been transported within a period of 5 million years.

6.5   Synthesis: time constraints on the Grampian phase

A constraint on the onset of collision is provided by a cooling age of c. 480 Ma obtained on the metamorphic sole of the Ballantrae ophiolite. Age constraints on the end of the Grampian collision event are provided by cessation of collision-related deformation and the onset of isostatic uplift in the Grampian Highlands, and by the arrival of the first erosive products from the mountain belt in nearby sedimentary basins. As direct dating of collision-related deformation fabrics is difficult, an age of c. 458 Ma, obtained from the oldest post-kinematic granite yet dated, can only provide an upper limit. The first arrival of metamorphic debris in the surrounding sedimentary basins is dated at c. 465 Ma and indicates that at this time the orogen was uplifting and eroding: collision had ceased. The Grampian phase in Scotland was therefore a short-lived, <15 million years (c. 480–465 Ma), 'catastrophic' event that resulted from the collision of an island arc with the Laurentian margin, an event that was coincident with ophiolite obduction, nappe tectonics, crustal thickening, metamorphism and magmatism.

6.6   How high were the Grampian mountains?

The metamorphic rocks that outcrop across the Grampian Highlands contain mineral assemblages that were formed at pressures of up to 1000 MPa (Figure 5.12), equivalent to crustal depths of some 35 km. Does this mean that these mountains once stood 35 km higher? Well, no. If the eroded 35 km of crust were to be put back in place, its weight would load the crust, and much of the added thickness would be accommodated by the crust being pushed down into the mantle rather than being simply added to the topographic height above sea-level. Because continental crust is less dense than the mantle, and is therefore buoyant, the crust behaves like an iceberg floating in the sea. Thick crust (like large icebergs) lies higher above sea-level and extends further below sea-level than thinner crust. This effect leads to an expected correlation between crustal thickness and mean elevation. The total thickness of crust in the Central Highlands Terrane would have comprised the present thickness (c. 30 km) plus the eroded 35 km, making c. 65 km in total. This is similar to the thickness of crust in Tibet (c. 55–70 km) and the Altiplano of South America (65 km), where the mean elevations above sea-level are 5.5 km and 4 km respectively. Following this argument, it is conceivable that the Grampian mountains, some 465 million years ago, were as high as the Himalaya are today.

6.7 Summary of Section 6

- Isotopic dating indicates that the rocks of the Dalradian Supergroup that were metamorphosed during the Grampian phase began to cool through their closure temperatures at c. 473 Ma and continued to cool until c. 400 Ma. The majority of the high-grade rocks passed through their closure temperatures at c. 470 Ma, shortly after the peak of Grampian metamorphism.

- Uplift following tectonic burial led to partial melting of metasediments, a process that culminated in the emplacement of a suite of post-kinematic c. 460–435 Ma granites.

- Detrital garnets in sediments from the Midland Valley and Southern Uplands Terranes have Barrovian-type compositions. These data indicate that the Grampian mountains were eroding and supplying metamorphic detritus as early as c. 465 Ma.

- The Grampian phase in Scotland was therefore a short-lived, <15 million years (c. 480–465 Ma), catastrophic event that resulted from the collision of an island arc with the Laurentian margin.

7   Sedimentation and tectonics at a mid-Ordovician to Silurian active margin

7.1   Introduction

In mid-Ordovician to Silurian times, the Grampian mountains underwent exhumation, uplift and erosion, and shed debris into the surrounding basins. While the mountains were being exhumed an active margin was developing to the south. At this time, continued plate convergence led to closure of the Iapetus Ocean and development of a northwards-dipping subduction zone, above which a series of island arcs and an accretionary prism developed. The Ordovician and Silurian rocks of the Midland Valley and Southern Uplands Terranes record the development of this active margin, which is the subject of this Section. Section 7.2 outlines the mid-Ordovician to Silurian sedimentary history of the Midland Valley Terrane. Section 7.3 concentrates on the sedimentary and tectonic evolution of the Southern Uplands Terrane. Section 7.4 gives a reconstruction of the regional geological framework for the mid-Ordovician to Silurian active margin.

7.2   Mid-Ordovician to Silurian sedimentation in the Midland Valley Terrane

The Middle Ordovician and Silurian rocks of the Midland Valley of Scotland are exposed in a series of small inliers in the southern part of the Midland Valley, shown in Figure 6.3. Although fragmentary in nature, a sedimentary history has been constructed by linking the information from these inliers.

7.2.1   Ordovician sedimentation

Middle Ordovician rocks rest unconformably on the Ballantrae Complex (Figure 5.5). Recalling Section 5.2.2, the lowermost units comprise Llanvirn to Caradoc (*c.* 470–450 Ma) conglomerates that were deposited from submarine fans into a subsiding basin. These conglomerates pass upwards and laterally into deeper-water turbiditic mudstones and sandstones. Lateral facies changes, thickness variations and palaeocurrent data indicate that sedimentation was partly fault-controlled, and of northerly derivation. The conglomerates contain a variety of clasts that originated from several sources. Clasts of ultrabasic and basic rocks were derived from the underlying Ballantrae Complex. There is also a suite of igneous clasts, ranging in composition from granites to diorites, whose geochemistry is consistent with an origin in a calc-alkaline magmatic arc. These clasts have been dated and give ages of *c.* 560–450 Ma. In addition, a considerable metamorphic component is represented by clasts of low-grade mica schists and abundant detrital garnets. As we saw in Section 6.4, the compositions of these garnets suggest that the metamorphic detritus was derived from the erosion of Dalradian metasediments. Taken together these data suggest that the Ordovician rocks of the Midland Valley were sourced from the erosion of the Grampian mountains, an active magmatic arc and the Ballantrae Complex.

7.2.2   Silurian sedimentation

The Silurian rocks of the Midland Valley comprise Llandovery turbidites that pass upwards into shallow-water fluvial deposits. Conglomerates were then deposited from terrestrial fans in Wenlock times. The lowermost units are dominated by clasts of volcanic rocks. Higher up in the succession the conglomerates contain predominantly metaquartzite clasts; at the highest levels exposed the clasts are mainly greywackes. Interestingly, palaeocurrent analysis and the northward thinning of these sequences suggest a southerly source for some of these deposits, a point we will return to in Section 7.4.3.

A similar history is recorded from the Silurian rocks (Wenlock to Ludlow in age) of Ireland (Figure 6.3) that lie unconformably on the ophiolite fragments and sediments of the South Mayo Trough (Section 5.2.2). Sedimentation started in mid-Llandovery times with a fluvial sequence of red cross-bedded sandstones, conglomerates and breccias deposited by braided rivers that flowed southwards. These sediments are overlain by marine sandstones and conglomerates deposited in delta-fan environments. Lithic clasts in the sandstones include metaquartzites, similar to those from Scotland, and porphyritic volcanic rocks. Volcanic ash layers are also present in the succession, and imply the presence of a nearby arc. Shallow-water sedimentation may have occurred in a series of small inter-arc basins.

7.2.3 Summary of Section 7.2

* The mid-Ordovician rocks of the Midland Valley were deposited in a subsiding fore-arc or inter-arc basin (the Midland Valley Basin). The sediments were derived from the north and were sourced from the Ballantrae Complex, the eroding Grampian mountains and an active magmatic arc.

* Silurian sedimentation occurred in a series of shallow-water inter-arc basins.

7.3 Sedimentation and tectonics in the Southern Uplands Terrane

The Southern Uplands Terrane comprises a series of SW–NE-striking slices of Ordovician and Silurian rocks. On a large scale the Southern Uplands is divided into three major fault-bounded blocks, the Northern, Central and Southern Belts (Figure 7.1). As a whole, there is an overall younging of the rocks from north to south across the terrane, with the Northern Belt containing Ordovician rocks, the Central Belt Ordovician and Silurian rocks, and the Southern Belt being entirely Silurian in age. Each of these belts is further subdivided into slices or tracts that are bounded by reverse faults or thrusts. The succession within each of these tracts generally youngs towards the north (Figure 7.1).

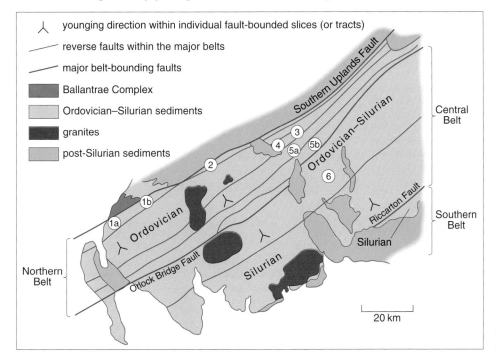

Figure 7.1 Simplified geological map of the Southern Uplands. The numbered units refer to the individual fault-bounded tracts in the Northern and Central Belts.

7.3.1 Sedimentation

The Northern Belt is bounded to the north by the Southern Uplands Fault and to the south by the Orlock Bridge Fault (Figure 7.1). The succession within each of the individual tracts of the Northern Belt is illustrated in Figure 7.2.

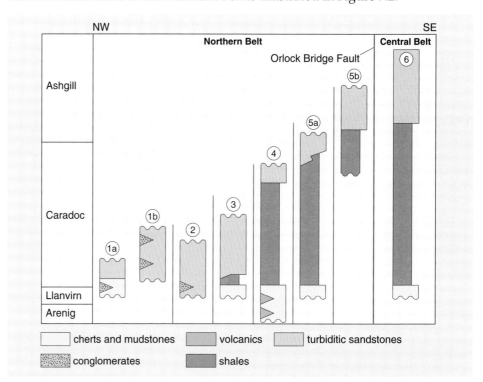

Figure 7.2 Ordovician stratigraphy of the Southern Uplands showing the fault-bounded tracts within the Northern and part of the Central Belt. The numbered columns relate to the tracts located in Figure 7.1.

Overall the succession comprises three distinct sedimentary units, although not all of them are found in every tract. The lowermost unit comprises pillow lavas and cherts that are interpreted as the uppermost part of the oceanic crust. These are overlain by deep-water black shales. The oceanic crust and black shales are overlain by conglomerates and turbiditic sandstones, which were deposited in submarine fans. Within the individual tracts, and from north to south, the influx of these turbidites occurs at progressively later times. In the northernmost tracts, the turbidites rest directly on the oceanic crust, and the shales are absent.

Petrographic studies of the major conglomeratic units have found that clasts of granites, volcanics, basalts and microgabbros are present. Many show similarities to the arc-related igneous rocks from the lowermost conglomerates that overlie the Ballantrae Complex. Turbidite sandstones are grey, quartz-rich and contain metamorphic detritus. The composition of detrital garnet is consistent with a Barrovian-type source; the presence of compositions typical of low-grade metamorphism in the older rocks and high-grade metamorphism in younger rocks is typical of unroofing sequences (Section 6.4). Ar-isotope dating of detrital micas gives ages of *c.* 480–460 Ma. These are similar to cooling ages from the Dalradian metasediments that were being uplifted to the north-west (Section 6.2). Palaeocurrent data point to a derivation from both the north-west and north-east.

Although the oldest sediments in the Central Belt are Caradoc to Ashgill, these are only a minor component, and the Central Belt mostly comprises Silurian greywackes and conglomerates deposited in submarine fans. The Southern Belt comprises Wenlock turbidites and thin siltstones.

7.3.2 The Southern Uplands as an accretionary prism?

The generally accepted interpretation of the Southern Uplands is that it represents an accretionary prism that developed in the fore-arc region of a convergent plate margin (Figure 7.3).

Accretionary prisms develop when trench-fill turbidites, ocean sediments and underlying oceanic crust are scraped from the descending oceanic plate by the leading edge of an overriding plate and become accreted to it. The internal structure of the prism therefore consists of a series of thrust-bounded slices that dip towards the arc and define wedge-shaped packets (Figure 7.3b). As subduction continues, the older thrusts and packets are gradually moved upwards and rotated as new wedges are added to the base of the prism. The older thrusts rotate to become steeper with time and may become inactive. Within each slice the sediments young towards the continent, whereas overall the age of sediments in the slices gets progressively younger towards the oceanward side. The different stratigraphies observed within each slice are consistent with deposition in widely separated parts of the ocean floor; eventually these are juxtaposed as they are progressively accreted to the subduction complex. During this deformation a fore-arc basin may develop between the trench and island arc.

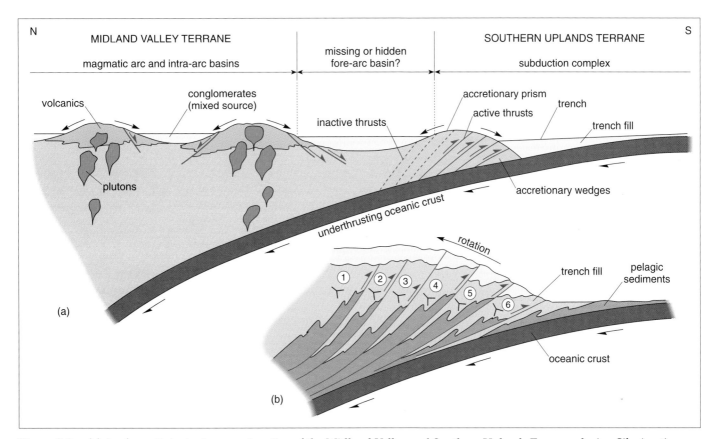

Figure 7.3   (a) A schematic tectonic reconstruction of the Midland Valley and Southern Uplands Terranes during Silurian times. (b) A model for the development of an accretionary prism at a convergent plate margin. The numbers refer to the order in which each tectonic slice was accreted.

7.3.3 Summary of Section 7.3

- The Southern Uplands comprises a series of Ordovician to Silurian sediments in a series of fault- or thrust-bounded slices.

- The sediments consist of a sequence of ocean-floor rocks that were progressively swamped by a turbidite apron. The petrology of clasts within the turbidites points to a significant component being derived from the erosion of Dalradian metasediments.

- The structure and sedimentology of the Southern Uplands is comparable to modern accretionary prisms that develop in convergent plate margins.

7.4 Interpretation: regional tectonic framework for the Midland Valley and Southern Uplands

7.4.1 Introduction

In mid-Ordovician to Silurian times an active margin developed to the south of the Grampian mountains. Several lines of evidence indicate that a volcanic arc developed in the Midland Valley, and was probably built on an older remnant Ordovician arc (Section 5.2.2) and metamorphic basement. The arc developed in response to northwards-directed subduction as indicated by the geometry of the Southern Uplands accretionary prism. Large amounts of sediments derived from the uplifting Grampian mountains and the volcanic arc were shed southwards into intra-arc basins and submarine fans, and ultimately incorporated into a growing accretionary prism. A simplified tectonic reconstruction of the active margin is presented in Figure 7.3a. Two important problems arise if this reconstruction is accurate. Firstly, what caused a reversal in the polarity (i.e. the direction) of subduction at the end of the Grampian phase? Secondly, where is the missing fore-arc basin?

7.4.2 What caused a subduction zone reversal?

In Figure 5.1 we saw that the Grampian phase resulted from the collision of an island arc with the Laurentian margin and that at this time the subduction zone dipped southwards. Given the evidence outlined above for the development of a N-dipping subduction zone it follows that at some point in the early Ordovician the subduction zone must have changed polarity. One possible explanation is that the collision of an island arc with the Laurentian margin led to jamming or blocking of the S-dipping subduction zone (Figure 5.1c). As a consequence of continued convergence, a second N-dipping subduction zone developed on the oceanward side of the island arc complex (Figure 5.1d).

7.4.3 A missing fore-arc basin?

The close proximity of the magmatic arc of the Midland Valley and the accretionary prism of the Southern Uplands causes a space problem for tectonic and palaeogeographic reconstructions if modern-day analogues are taken into consideration. In active modern-day intra-oceanic subduction zones the distance between the magmatic arc and the trench is at least c. 90 km, and this gap is normally occupied by a fore-arc basin (Figure 7.3a). In Scotland this fore-arc basin is missing. Additional evidence for a piece of missing crust comes from the study of the Silurian conglomerates of the Midland Valley (Section 7.2.3). The southerly-derived mixed metaquartzite and volcanic clasts could not have come from the Southern Uplands, as rocks of this type are not present there. They were probably derived from a volcanic arc built on a metamorphic basement (a Midland Valley-type crust) that is no longer exposed.

One possible explanation is that the missing crust now lies below the Southern Uplands accretionary prism. Two lines of evidence support this concept. Firstly, the presence of xenoliths of granulite-facies rocks that occur in Carboniferous volcanic vents in the Southern Uplands lends support to the existence of continental basement at depth. Secondly, a large scale S-dipping reflector identified in geophysical profiles taken across the Southern Uplands has been interpreted as a large-scale thrust that translated the accretionary prism northwards during the later collision of Avalonian fragments with the Laurentian margin (Figure 7.4).

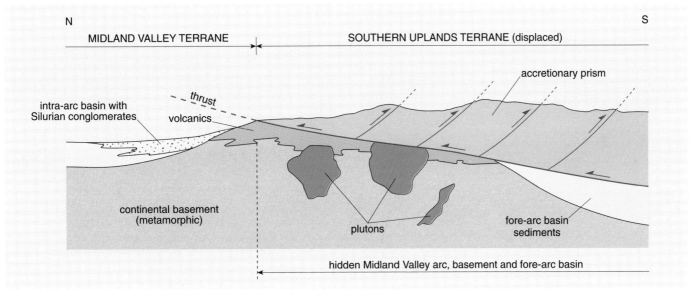

Figure 7.4   A tectonic reconstruction explaining the present juxtaposition of the Midland Valley arc and the Southern Uplands accretionary prism.

7.5   Summary of Section 7

• In mid-Ordovician to Silurian times an active margin developed on the southern side of the Laurentian margin.

• The continued closure of the Iapetus Ocean was achieved by the development of a second, N-dipping, subduction zone on the oceanward side of an island arc that collided with the Laurentian margin.

• A series of magmatic arcs, fore-arc and intra-arc basins formed in the Midland Valley, and in the Southern Uplands an accretionary prism developed as a result of the continued northwards subduction.

8 Multiple plate collisions and the end of the Iapetus Ocean

8.1 Introduction

Sections 4 to 7 outlined the evidence and possible plate-tectonic explanations for the formation and partial closure of the Iapetus Ocean. Section 4 showed that a prolonged period of rifting that started in late Precambrian times culminated in plate separation and led to the opening, to the south of Laurentia, of the Iapetus Ocean. The initial stage of ocean closure was by subduction of oceanic crust and the collision of an island arc with Laurentia, which caused the Grampian phase of the Caledonian Orogeny (Section 5). Ocean closure continued with the development of a northwards-dipping subduction zone on the southern margin of Laurentia (Section 7). This Section concentrates on establishing the plate-tectonic causes for the demise and eventual closure of the Iapetus Ocean in the early Palaeozoic. Section 8.2 presents a broad, plate-scale view of the causes of the closure, whereas the later Sections give the geological evidence upon which these plate models are based. Section 8.8 summarizes the closure of the Iapetus Ocean.

8.2 Palaeocontinental reconstructions

8.2.1 The global view

Palaeocontinental reconstructions of plate movements since the late Precambrian are based in part on palaeomagnetic pole positions, and partly on studies of fossils that allow palaeogeographically separate faunal provinces to be recognized. The palaeogeographic reconstructions that are relevant to events associated with the Caledonian Orogeny were illustrated in Section 1 (Figure 1.5) and involve many continental fragments that bordered Iapetus and which were converging during the early to mid-Palaeozoic. Of these continental fragments, Baltica and Eastern Avalonia were directly involved in the geological evolution of Scotland. Further to the west, Western Avalonia collided in mid-Silurian times with Laurentia, and Armorica collided with the assembled northern fragments to the south-east, forming a palaeocontinent informally termed Laurussia, in the Early Devonian. In mid-Devonian times Iberia collided with Armorica.

8.2.2 A model for the closure of the Iapetus Ocean

In recent years a detailed evaluation of the causes and nature of the closure of the Iapetus Ocean has been based on a multidisciplinary approach incorporating stratigraphic, structural and isotopic dating methods applied to rocks from a huge area. Figure 8.1 shows the sequence of convergence of continental fragments onto the Laurentian margin during Silurian to Early Devonian times.

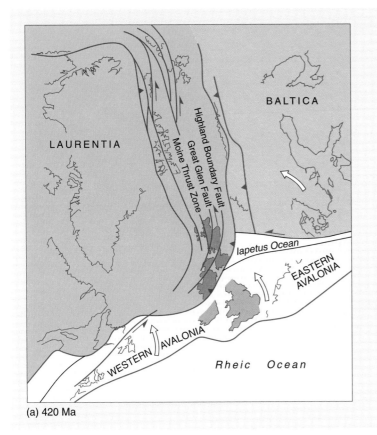
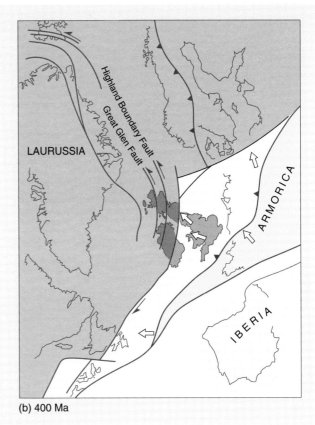

(a) 420 Ma   (b) 400 Ma

Figure 8.1   Reconstruction of multiple plate collisions and the Silurian closure of the Iapetus Ocean. (a) 420 Ma, at about the Wenlock–Ludlow boundary. Large arrows indicate the convergence directions of Baltica and Eastern Avalonia with the Laurentian margin. (b) 400 Ma, Early Devonian, showing the Acadian convergence directions. Also shown is the impending collision of Iberia with Armorica, which occurred in Mid-Devonian times. These diagrams illustrate the progressive restriction and closure of the Iapetus Ocean.

● Study Figure 8.1a. Does it indicate orthogonal plate convergence (i.e. perpendicular to plate boundaries) with the Laurentian margin?

● No. Examination of the plate convergence directions indicates that in mid-Silurian times (Figure 8.1a) Baltica collided obliquely with the north-eastern part of the Laurentian margin.

The collision of Laurentia and Baltica led to the closure of the northern arm of the Iapetus Ocean, an event called the Scandian orogenic phase, and was responsible for mountain building in Norway, Sweden and East Greenland. Further south, and at the same time, Eastern Avalonia collided obliquely with the Laurentian margin. In both cases a significant component of anticlockwise rotation was involved in the displacement. One of the major consequences of oblique collision was that major plate movements were accommodated along a series of major strike–slip faults and shear zones (Box 8.1).

Box 8.1 Contrasting the effects of orthogonal and oblique convergence

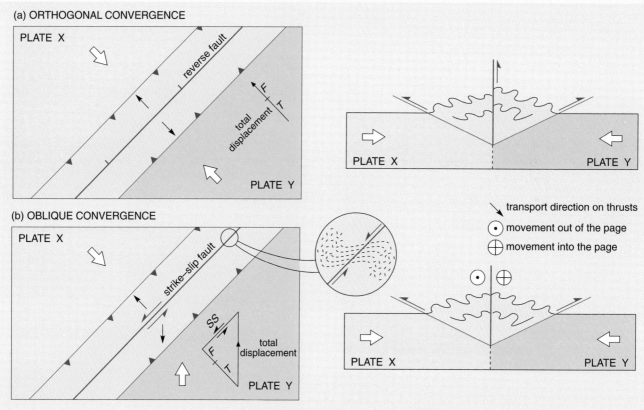

Figure 8.2   Models of collision between two plates X and Y: (a) orthogonal convergence; (b) oblique convergence in map view (left) and cross-section (right). The total amount of shortening accommodated by thrusting (*T*), folding (*F*) and strike–slip displacements (*SS*) is shown by the vector diagrams. The symbols in circles indicate sinistral strike–slip displacement. The inset shows how the sense of displacement along the fault is indicated by the rotation of fabric components.

In a simple model of plate convergence, two blocks representing two plates X and Y collide in an orthogonal manner, essentially head-on (Figure 8.2a). In this model, crustal shortening across the orogen is accommodated by reverse and thrust faulting, and by folding. During an orthogonal collision, shortening is perpendicular or normal to plate boundaries (termed orogen-normal shortening) such that the transport directions on faults are perpendicular to the plate margin.

But what would happen if plates X and Y collided obliquely? This situation is illustrated in Figure 8.2b. One of the major consequences of oblique collision is that plate movements can be resolved into two components, a component of orogen-normal shortening and a component of orogen-parallel displacement or shear. In this case, the orogen-normal shortening is accommodated by folding and thrusting (which may be dip–slip or oblique), whereas an orogen-parallel component is accommodated along strike–slip faults or shear zones. In Figure 8.2b, an anticlockwise shear is imposed on the orogen because of the angular

relationship between the plates, and strike–slip faults will have a sinistral sense of displacement. The sense of displacement on these structures can be determined from the sense of rotation of fabric components into the fault or shear zone. During oblique convergence or collision, material is moved along the orogen.

In reality, the style and location of structures that develop along a collisional plate boundary are a function of a variety of factors, including the angle of convergence, the shape of the plate boundary, the existence of pre-collisional weaknesses (e.g. faults) and the nature and strength of the crust. For instance, Figure 8.3 shows the effects of an orthogonal plate convergence in which the plate boundary has a promontory and re-entrant.

Note how the sense of displacement is different on either side of the promontory and re-entrant, being either sinistral (anticlockwise) or dextral (clockwise). The relative displacements on the strike–slip faults indicate that material is transferred away from the promontory and towards the re-entrant.

The combination of compression (shortening) and strike–slip displacement is called transpression; likewise a combination of extension and strike–slip displacement is called transtension. In the example in Figure 8.3, the formation of structures on both sides of the promontory would result from either dextral or sinistral transpression, yet plate convergence is, overall, orthogonal. This example shows that the relative motion of the plates cannot simply be established from the kinematics of fault displacement from different parts of a collision zone. Independent information such as the results of palaeomagnetic studies must be considered.

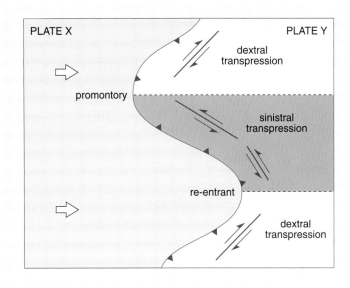

Figure 8.3   Orientation and sense of displacement along structures developed during orthogonal convergence involving a plate with an irregular boundary, containing a promontory and a re-entrant.

By Late Silurian–Early Devonian times (Figure 8.1b) the extent of the Iapetus Ocean was severely restricted and, with respect to Britain and Ireland, was essentially closed. It is clear from the comparison of Figures 8.1a and b that the Iapetus Ocean closed in a scissor-like manner, with closure first in the south-west and progressing north-eastwards. This closure was a consequence of the oblique convergence and anticlockwise rotation of Eastern Avalonia into a re-entrant along the Laurentian margin. In Early Devonian times (c. 400 Ma) further compression between Eastern Avalonia and Laurentia led to the Acadian orogenic phase. The cause of this event is uncertain, but two possibilities have been put forward: either convergence of Eastern Avalonia with Laurentia continued for some time after ocean closure, or this compression was enhanced by the collision of Armorica with Eastern Avalonia in Early Devonian times.

The change in displacement along major strike–slip faults with time indicates an anticlockwise change in convergence directions. Evidence for this change can be seen in Figure 8.1, where the direction of displacement along the strike–slip fault in Newfoundland, associated with collision of Western Avalonia and Laurentia, changes from sinistral (Figure 8.1a) to dextral (Figure 8.1b). In essence, the convex shape of the Laurentian margin controlled the direction of displacements along the strike–slip faults. In Britain and Ireland, the Acadian compression induced further sinistral strike–slip displacements along major faults, e.g. the Highland Boundary Fault, and in some cases reactivation of older faults, e.g. the Great Glen Fault, a feature that is accentuated around the 'convex corner' of the Laurentian margin.

What, then, are the tectonic implications for the Scottish Highlands of significant displacements (>c. 100 km) along the Great Glen and Highland Boundary Faults? An important consequence of significant sinistral displacements along these major faults is that during Silurian times the Northern Highlands lay further to the north-east and were located opposite Scandinavia. This palaeogeography makes it likely that the deformation in the Moine Thrust Zone may have resulted from the collision of Baltica with Laurentia, and did not form in response to the collision of Eastern Avalonia and Laurentia.

8.2.3 Summary of Section 8.2

- Plate reconstructions indicate that the closure of the Iapetus Ocean in the early Palaeozoic resulted from multiple plate collisions.

- Plate-tectonic models suggest that plate collision was predominantly oblique. As a consequence, Iapetus closed in a scissor-like manner.

- The combination of oblique collision and the shape of the plate boundary ultimately controlled the nature of the deformation, in particular the sense of displacement along major strike–slip faults.

- Given the suggested magnitude of the sinistral displacements along some of these faults, it seems likely that the Northern Highlands lay within the Baltica–Laurentia collision zone.

8.3   Tectonics of the Northern Highlands

The geology of north-west Scotland provides a glimpse into the processes active during the early Palaeozoic collision of Baltica and Laurentia. This Section describes the structures, metamorphism and magmatism that resulted from this collision.

8.3.1 Structure and metamorphism of the Northern Highlands

Although complex in detail, the main lithotectonic units and structures of the Northern Highlands can be traced along strike over great distances. These structures are illustrated in Figure 8.4, where they are seen to separate major lithotectonic units.

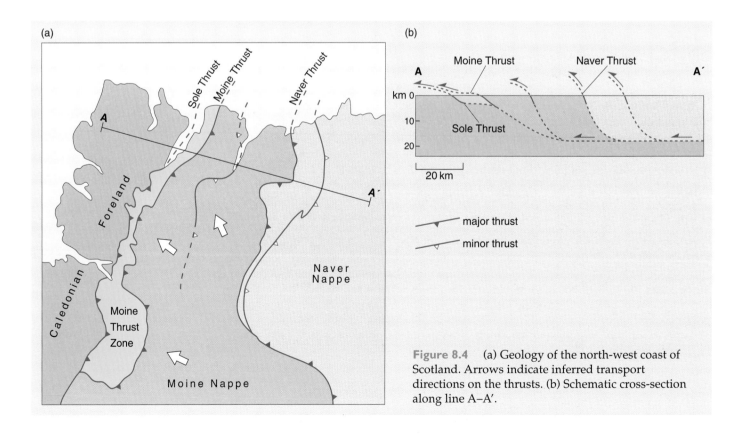

Figure 8.4   (a) Geology of the north-west coast of Scotland. Arrows indicate inferred transport directions on the thrusts. (b) Schematic cross-section along line A–A'.

The Moine Thrust separates the Moine rocks of the Moine and Naver Nappes from the deformed Lewisian, Torridonian and Cambrian–Ordovician rocks of the Moine Thrust Zone. The Sole Thrust, the lowermost thrust of the Moine Thrust Zone, separates the rocks of the Moine Thrust Zone from the essentially undeformed rocks exposed further west. The Moine Thrust Zone directly underlies the Moine Thrust and comprises a series of major thrusts and smaller imbricate thrusts that are stacked on top of each other and carry deformed Lewisian, Torridonian and Cambrian–Ordovician rocks towards the west (Figure 8.5). Thrusting was active at shallow levels in the crust, as indicated by syn-kinematic lower greenschist-facies assemblages.

(a)

(b)

Figure 8.5   Structures within the Moine Thrust Zone at Whitten Head, north-west Scotland. (a) Internal imbrication of Cambrian quartzites of the Pipe Rock (Eriboll Sandstone Formation). View looking north, height of cliffs 150 m. (b) Thrust placing Lewisian basement over Cambrian quartzites of the Pipe Rock (Eriboll Sandstone Formation). View looking south, height of cliffs 150 m.

The Moine and Naver Nappes are internally imbricated by a series of lesser thrusts. These structurally higher-level (and earlier) thrusts are ductile structures that were active at higher metamorphic grades (deeper levels in the crust), as indicated in Figure 8.4b. Syn-kinematic temperatures obtained from the thrusts decrease from east to west, a feature consistent with deformation progressing from deeper to shallower levels as rocks were transported towards the west. Microstructure and fabric analysis indicates that Barrovian-type metamorphism was syn-kinematic with the ductile thrusting. The sequence of mineral growth of garnet→staurolite→kyanite is consistent with increasing P and T resulting from crustal thickening by ductile thrusting.

8.3.2 Magmatism and the timing of deformation

A series of intrusive bodies are found above and below the Naver Thrust. These occur as a series of branching sheets and lenses that are sub-concordant with the major thrust planes. They comprise medium- to coarse-grained granites, granodiorites and diorites. The sheets cross-cut early fold structures and fabrics that developed in response to the initial stages of crustal shortening, yet are themselves deformed and carry fabrics that resulted from tectonic strains induced during the later stages of thrusting. As such, these granites are thought to have been emplaced synchronously with ductile thrusting. Radiometric dating of the syn-kinematic intrusions has given ages in the range c. 435–420 Ma. Mica cooling ages (Rb–Sr method) from the various nappes indicate a range of c. 440–410 Ma and cooling ages on micas (formed during thrusting) from the Moine Thrust Zone are c. 428–413 Ma. The similarity between these ages suggests that the metamorphism, magmatism and displacement along the ductile thrusts and the Moine Thrust Zone belong to the same sequence of deformation. These ages are a good deal younger (by at least 30 million years) than those of the Grampian phase and indicate that these events belong to the younger mid-Silurian Scandian phase of the Caledonian Orogeny.

8.3.3 Regional implications

The Moine Thrust and its associated ductile thrusts formed at c. 435–420 Ma during the Scandian phase, which resulted from the collision of Baltica and Laurentia. A similar history of thrusting, Barrovian-type metamorphism and

Figure 8.6   A simplified tectonic model for the Scandian phase of the Caledonian Orogeny (c. 435–420 Ma) in northern Scotland. (a) Development of an active margin in post-Grampian times by westwards subduction of the northern arm of Iapetus beneath Laurentia. (b) Underthrusting of Baltica beneath Laurentia and the development of both E- and W-directed thrust systems.

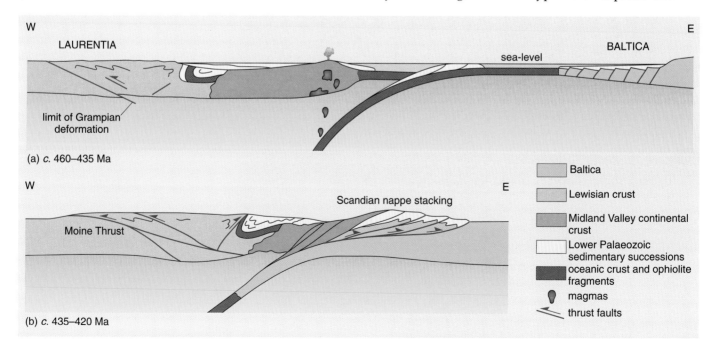

magmatism is recorded in both East Greenland and Scandinavia, where the Scandian phase lasted until *c.* 390 Ma. The Scandian event was initiated by westward subduction of the northern arm of the Iapetus Ocean beneath the Laurentian margin (Figure 8.6a). Continued compression led to continental collision with crustal shortening being accommodated by thrusting towards both the west and east (Figure 8.6b).

8.3.4 Summary of Section 8.3

- Thrusting, metamorphism and magmatism in north-west Scotland (*c.* 435–420 Ma) are attributed to the Scandian phase of the Caledonian Orogeny.

- Crustal thickening was achieved by thrusting and resulted in Barrovian-type metamorphism.

8.4 Silurian–Devonian strike–slip displacements on the Laurentian margin

Section 8.2.2 pointed to the importance of strike–slip faulting during multiple plate collisions. In this Section we describe the nature and establish the timing of these displacements on the Laurentian margin.

8.4.1 Geometry and amount of displacement

The Laurentian margin is cut by a series of steeply-dipping faults that strike roughly NE–SW, and cut most of the other Caledonian structures (e.g. the Great Glen Fault and the Highland Boundary Fault – Fair Head–Clew Bay Line, Figure 8.7).

- Do these faults have a consistent strike along their length?

- These faults exhibit major strike swings from N–S in Shetland to E–W in Ireland.

As we have seen, this strike swing may be linked to the deformation around the convex corner of the Laurentian margin. Geophysical evidence indicates that these faults extend to depths of at least 40 km. Many have a protracted history. For example, the Highland Boundary Fault – Fair Head–Clew Bay Line may originally have defined the southern limit of rifted Proterozoic crust, and represents a site of collisional suture during the Grampian event. In the Late Silurian to Early Devonian, displacements along the fault led to juxtaposition of the Midland Valley Terrane against the Central Highlands Terrane. The use of structural analysis on granitic plutons, along with the correlation of distinct geological features across these faults, indicates they have undergone significant sinistral displacements. Estimates for the amount of displacement range from *c.* 10 km on the Strathconan Fault, to *c.* 40 km on the Leannan Fault to hundreds of kilometres for the Great Glen and Highland Boundary Faults.

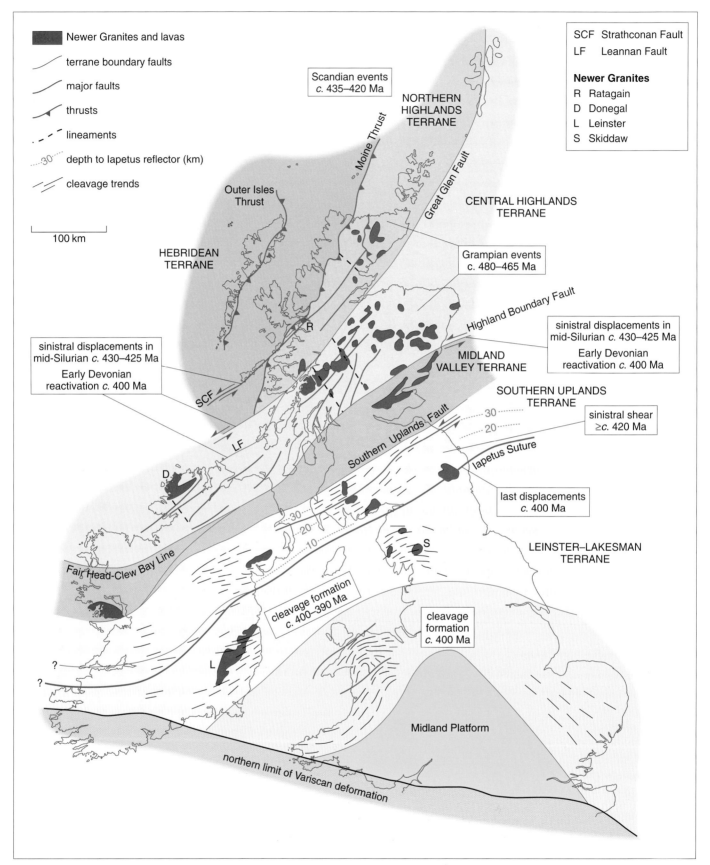

Figure 8.7   Map of Britain and Ireland showing Caledonian structures based on surface geology, borehole data and geophysical studies. The timing of deformation and the location of the Newer Granites is also shown.

8.4.2 Time constraints on fault zone displacements

Early displacements on the Great Glen Fault and associated faults are constrained by the ages of syn-kinematic intrusions. Figure 8.8 shows an example of one of these granites, the Ratagain granite, which is found adjacent to the Strathconan Fault (for location see Figure 8.7).

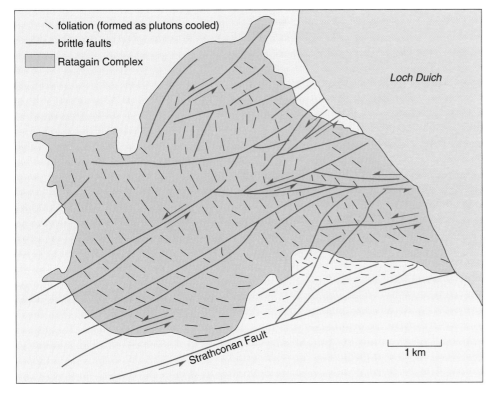

Figure 8.8   Relationship of the Ratagain granite to the Strathconan Fault.

The *c.* 425 Ma Ratagain granite has been deformed by both ductile and brittle structures (Figure 8.8). The first deformation produced a strong ductile foliation that formed as the granite was cooling and crystallizing. The anticlockwise swing of this foliation towards the fault is consistent with a sinistral sense of displacement within a ductile shear zone. The Ratagain granite and its ductile foliation are cut by a network of later brittle faults that exhibit a sinistral offset. These faults were active during the emplacement of a series of mafic dykes that have been dated at between *c.* 410 Ma and *c.* 395 Ma (Early Devonian). The conclusion from this is that a mid-Silurian (*c.* 425 Ma) shear zone was reactivated as a brittle fault during later Early Devonian (*c.* 410–395 Ma) displacements. Data from other syn-kinematic granites, including the Donegal granite (Figure 8.7), support the conclusion that sinistral strike–slip displacement occurred in two distinct episodes, at *c.* 430–425 Ma and *c.* 405–390 Ma.

8.4.3 Sinistral displacements in the Southern Uplands

Limited constraints can also be placed on the timing of deformation across the Southern Uplands accretionary prism. As we saw in Section 7.3.2, the progressive accretion of thrust slices to the toe of the accretionary prism led to the steepening and rotation of earlier thrusts (Figure 7.3). Many of these steepened thrusts (including the Orlock Bridge Fault) record later sinistral strike–slip reactivations. Time constraints on these displacements are provided by the age of post-kinematic granites (*c.* 410–390 Ma), and of mafic dykes (*c.* 420–398 Ma), which can only provide a minimum age for the last sinistral strike–slip displacements along these faults.

8.4.4 Summary of Section 8.4

- A series of major sinistral strike–slip faults cuts the Laurentian margin.

- Age constraints from syn-kinematic intrusions suggest that sinistral displacement occurred in two discrete episodes, in mid-Silurian and in Early Devonian times.

8.5 Collision of Eastern Avalonia with the Laurentian margin

The model presented in Section 8.2 suggests that Eastern Avalonia collided obliquely with the Laurentian margin and that this led to a scissor-like closure of the Iapetus Ocean. This Section outlines the history of convergence and collision as seen in the sedimentary record of rocks on the Eastern Avalonian margin. The location of the Iapetus Suture Zone is also discussed.

8.5.1 The sedimentary record of a far-felt collision

The initial impingement of Eastern Avalonia on the Laurentian margin occurred somewhere to the south-west of Britain and Ireland in late Llandovery times (Figure 8.9), and the first effects of this collision are preserved in sedimentary basins along the Eastern Avalonian margin. Collision led to the reactivation of pre-existing fault systems causing compression, uplift and renewal of sedimentary sources in some areas, and extension, subsidence and deposition in others. Active basin-bounding faults became localized sites for late Llandovery turbidite sedimentation. The influx of turbidites began in late Llandovery times from a westerly source as collision somewhere to the south-west of Britain led to uplift and erosion. A major sedimentary influx was also derived from the south and was sourced from the erosion of uplifting crustal blocks. The relative timing of the turbidite influx is illustrated in Figure 8.10. This pattern of faulting and sedimentation was a response to the flexing of the crust in front of the collision zone, a direct result of thrust loading and subduction along the collision zone.

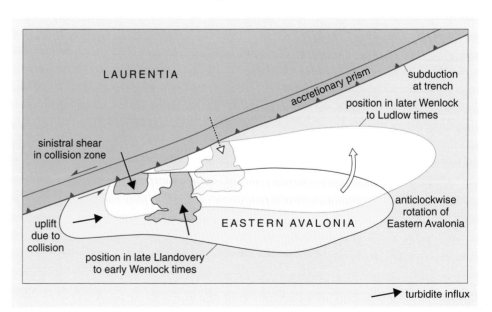

Figure 8.9 The palaeogeography of the Laurentian margin in Silurian times.

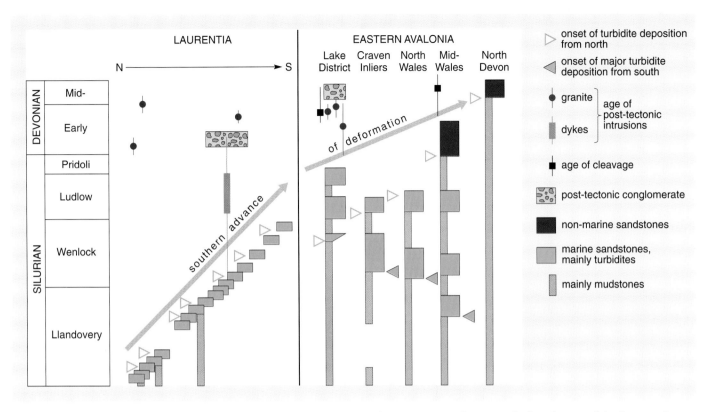

Figure 8.10 Timing of key events on the Laurentian and Eastern Avalonian margins during and after closure of the Iapetus Ocean.

8.5.2 Diachronous collision and terrane linkage

One estimate of the timing and nature of collision is provided by the date at which large volumes of sand-dominated turbidites first crossed the Iapetus Suture and were deposited on the Eastern Avalonian margin. The influx of northerly-derived sediments first occurred in Ireland in early Wenlock times and in north-west England in Wenlock–Ludlow times (illustrated schematically in Figure 8.9). These data suggest that closure of the Iapetus Ocean progressed from south-west to north-east; the closure was diachronous. By mid-Wenlock times, the trench was transformed into a foreland basin with the northern edge being marked by the Southern Uplands accretionary prism. Collision by the late Silurian (Wenlock to Ludlow) is indicated by a major reduction of convergence rates, as deduced from palaeomagnetic data, from $c.$ 12 cm yr^{-1} to <6.3 cm yr^{-1}, as underthrusting of Eastern Avalonia under Laurentia began. This also coincided with a change in the character and a reduction in the rate of sedimentation in mid- to late Wenlock times in the Southern Belt of the Southern Uplands, a feature that resulted from the slowing of subduction as a result of the onset of collision.

8.5.3 Sediment dispersal and basin shallowing

A unified depositional system was established across Britain by Wenlock times, as coarse debris derived from the uprising collision zone spread progressively southwards (Figure 8.10). In the late Silurian, basin subsidence slowed and gave way to shortening and uplift, with marine sedimentary basins being transformed into areas of non-marine sedimentation. Basin shallowing probably resulted from a combination of factors including an overall fall in sea-level and an increased rate of sediment supply.

8.5.4 Where is the Iapetus Suture?

The suture zone between Laurentia and Eastern Avalonia is the least exposed of all the major Caledonian terrane boundaries, but is usually drawn along a line parallel with the Solway Firth (Figure 8.7). The position of the suture zone is based on several lines of evidence. The suture must lie to the south of the Southern Uplands accretionary prism, as these sediments were scraped off the ocean floor and onto the Laurentian margin before collision. Seismic surveys show a prominent northwards-dipping reflector that is interpreted as separating southern and northern crust and is consistent with the Eastern Avalonian crust having underthrust the Laurentian margin (Figure 8.11).

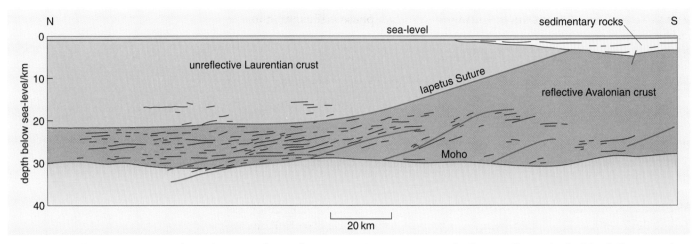

Figure 8.11   The interpretation of a N-dipping reflector from a seismic survey across the Iapetus Suture in the North Sea east of the Southern Uplands. The depth to this reflector is indicated in Figure 8.7.

In the north-west Isle of Man, Ordovician rocks of the Avalonian margin are overthrust by mid-Silurian strata akin to those of similar age in the Southern Uplands. The position of the suture across Ireland is less certain but is drawn between Ordovician inliers with either Laurentian or Avalonian faunal affinities. In south-west Ireland the suture is usually drawn along the Shannon Estuary, although a deep reflector has been located to the north of the Dingle Peninsula. These alternative locations are indicated in Figure 8.7. An age of *c.* 400 Ma obtained on volcanics from the Cheviot Hills that overlie the suture constrains the timing of final movements along this structure.

8.5.5 Summary of Section 8.5

- The collision of Eastern Avalonia with Laurentia initially occurred somewhere to the south-west of Britain and Ireland. Widespread turbidite sedimentation into basins on the Eastern Avalonian margin preserves a record of this collision.

- Collision was diachronous, with Iapetus closing in a scissor-like manner, progressing from south-west to north-east.

- After collision, northerly-derived detritus spread progressively southwards with time.

- Further or continued convergence led to basin shallowing and deposition of non-marine sedimentary sequences.

8.6   Late Silurian to Early Devonian deformation of Eastern Avalonia

The rocks on the Eastern Avalonian margin have been affected by a major deformation event that is referred to as the Acadian phase of the Caledonian Orogeny. The deformation is characterized by the regional development of folding, cleavage formation and associated low-grade, sub-greenschist facies (200–300 °C) metamorphism.

8.6.1   The cleavage pattern

The pattern of cleavage produced during the Acadian phase is illustrated in Figure 8.7.

● Is there a consistent trend to the cleavage?

● The general trend of the Acadian cleavage is NE–SW but significant deflections from this trend occur, e.g. around the Midland Platform, and in North Wales and the Lake District.

The general trend of the folds and cleavage is indicative of NW–SE crustal shortening across the orogen. The most obvious swing in the cleavage trend is around the old continental block of the Midland Platform. The platform is thought to have acted as an indenter against which the relatively 'soft', early Palaeozoic basins were moulded during shortening. A similar interpretation has been advanced for the arcuate swings in the cleavage pattern in North Wales and the Lake District. Here, older bodies of granite have acted as the rigid bodies around which the cleavage was moulded.

8.6.2   Time constraints on cleavage formation and deformation

The timing of cleavage formation is constrained by radiometric ages of syn-kinematic intrusions. The Skiddaw granite (c. 390 Ma) of the Lake District was emplaced during cleavage formation, as indicated by the timing of andalusite growth in hornfelses from its thermal aureole. In Ireland, the Leinster granite (c. 404 Ma) was intruded into an actively deforming sinistral shear zone. These data suggest that deformation and sinistral shear affected the Eastern Avalonian continental margin in Early Devonian times at c. 405–390 Ma.

Examination of Figure 8.10 indicates that deformation progressed from north to south with time during Late Silurian to Devonian times. An important point of this diagram is that at the same time as deformation was occurring in the Lake District, basins further south were shallowing and non-marine sediments were being deposited. Deformation of these non-marine sequences occurred somewhat later. Figure 8.10 also shows the timing of deformation across the Southern Uplands. One possible interpretation of this data set is that a wave of deformation spread southwards with time.

8.6.3   Summary of Section 8.6

• Eastern Avalonia was affected by the Acadian deformation event in the Late Silurian to Early Devonian.

• The timing of Acadian cleavage formation is constrained by the ages of syn-kinematic granites.

• Cleavage formation and deformation were diachronous. One interpretation is that a wave of deformation spread southwards with time.

8.7   Granite magmatism and convergence

So far we have seen that magmatism associated with the Scandian and Acadian phases spanned a time interval of *c.* 440–390 Ma. This extensive magmatic suite is collectively referred to as the Newer Granites. The distribution of the Newer Granites and associated lavas is presented in Figure 8.7. The age of the granites varies across the orogen. Granites in the Northern Highlands and Leinster–Lakesman Terranes range from *c.* 440–390 Ma whereas those in the Central Highlands, Midland Valley and Southern Uplands Terranes range from *c.* 420–380 Ma. But what can we learn from studying the geochemistry of these magmas?

8.7.1   Origin of the Newer Granites

In Figure 6.2 the initial $^{87}Sr/^{86}Sr$ ratios of the <*c.* 435 Ma Newer Granites and lavas is compared with those of the older >*c.* 435 Ma Ordovician (Grampian) granites from the Central and Northern Highlands.

- Can you suggest a reason for the differences in the initial $^{87}Sr/^{86}Sr$ ratios?

- The Newer Granites have very different isotopic signatures from the Ordovician granites in having lower initial $^{87}Sr/^{86}Sr$ ratios (0.704–0.708). These lower values are consistent with a major mantle component contributing to their genesis.

In addition, the Newer Granites have other geochemical characteristics, e.g. high Rb/Sr, high K/Na and low K/Rb ratios, that are indicative of calc-alkaline magmas produced in an Andean-type subduction zone, i.e. where oceanic lithosphere subducts below continental lithosphere. The Newer Granites probably owe their genesis to melting in response to the northwards-directed subduction of the Iapetus Ocean. Therefore, by *c.* 435 Ma the northwards-dipping subduction zone that started to form at the end of the Grampian phase had reached far beneath the Laurentian margin. However, the model of simple subduction and arc-related magmatism does not easily explain the plutons that occur close to the suture in the Southern Uplands and south of the suture in the Leinster–Lakesman Terrane. There is no general consensus as to the origin of these granites.

8.7.2 Summary of Section 8.7

- Magmatism spanning *c.* 440–390 Ma (the Newer Granites) probably resulted from melting in response to northwards-directed subduction of the Iapetus Ocean. By *c.* 435 Ma the subduction zone reached far to the north of the Central Highlands.

8.8   Summary of Section 8

The demise and eventual closure of the Iapetus Ocean resulted from a complex sequence of events caused by the accretion of several continental fragments to the Laurentian margin. A plate-tectonic model that attempts to summarize these events is presented in Figure 8.12 and a summary chronology is outlined below.

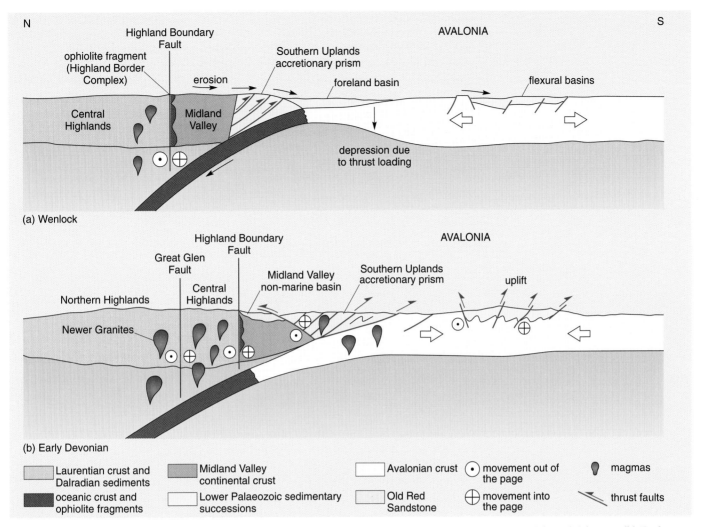

Figure 8.12 A plate-tectonic model for the Silurian–Devonian evolution of the Caledonian Orogen. (a) Mid-Silurian; (b) Early Devonian.

In Llandovery times, Baltica and Eastern Avalonia collided obliquely with the Laurentian margin. In north-west Scotland, the oblique collision with Baltica (the Scandian event) led to closure of the northern arm of the Iapetus Ocean by W-directed subduction. Continued convergence led to plate collision and resulted in NW-directed thrusting and the onset of sinistral strike–slip displacements. In the south, Eastern Avalonia was colliding with part of Laurentia south-west of the Southern Uplands. The Iapetus Ocean closed diachronously, progressing from south-west to north-east.

In Wenlock (Figure 8.12a) to Early Devonian times, strike–slip shear zones played a dominant role in the siting of granites on the Laurentian margin. The northern edge of Eastern Avalonia began to subduct beneath the accretionary prism of the Southern Uplands. A foreland basin developed in a depression in front of the loaded crust. Northerly-derived sediments spread progressively southwards.

Later, in the Early Devonian, the whole orogen underwent sinistral shear deformation (Figure 8.12b). On the Laurentian margin, deformation led to major sinistral reactivation of existing faults and juxtaposition of the southern terranes against the Central Highlands Terrane along the Highland Boundary Fault. In

Eastern Avalonia, deformation (referred to as the Acadian event) at this time led to cleavage formation and magmatism. Granites were emplaced synchronously with cleavage formation and sinistral displacements along shear zones. The Acadian event resulted from either prolonged post-collisional convergence between Eastern Avalonia and Laurentia, or was enhanced by further collision of Armorica with the southern edge of Eastern Avalonia. Non-marine Devonian sedimentation deposited the Old Red Sandstone, which is the subject of Section 9.

9 Sedimentation at the end of the Caledonian Orogeny

9.1 Introduction

The normal consequence of crustal thickening and mountain building is uplift and erosion. As long as uplift is faster than erosion, mountains will continue to grow, but once uplift slows, erosion eventually leads to the exhumation of the deeper roots of mountain belts. The exposure of these deep roots has allowed geologists to investigate the processes that led to crustal thickening and mountain building, as we have seen in this book. But what of the sediments that result from uplift and erosion during and after a period of prolonged mountain building? In this Section, we consider the drainage and sediment dispersal pattern associated with the final stages of the Caledonian Orogeny, as recorded by Devonian sedimentary rocks.

9.2 The Old Red Sandstone and the Devonian Period

The term Old Red Sandstone is the name given to the non-marine clastic sediments of approximately Devonian age that were deposited in the region where Baltica, Laurentia and Avalonia had collided during the Ordovician and Silurian Periods. These sediments are often brown to red in colour and comprise conglomerates (such as those shown in Figure 9.1), sandstones and siltstones

Figure 9.1   A bedding plane in an Upper Old Red Sandstone conglomerate that contains clasts of Dalradian metasediments, near Loch Lomond.

that are readily interpreted to be late- to post-orogenic sedimentary successions formed by intense erosion of the recently-built Caledonian mountains.

The Old Red Sandstone (ORS) is conventionally divided into the Lower, Middle and Upper Old Red Sandstone, but these only crudely equate with subdivisions of the Devonian. Furthermore, many Lower Old Red Sandstone successions were actually deposited during the Late Silurian, when the transition from marine to non-marine environments occurred. Some Upper Old Red Sandstone successions include rocks deposited in the Early Carboniferous.

9.3   Distribution and stratigraphy of the Late Silurian to Devonian Basins

The distribution of Late Silurian to Devonian sedimentary basins is illustrated in Figure 9.2a. The basins are classified according to whether they lie to the north or south of the Iapetus Suture; those to the north are termed internal basins, those to the south are external basins.

The history of sedimentation in these basins is reflected in the stratigraphic logs in Figure 9.2b, which show that the most continuous record of sedimentation is found in the south, in the Cornubian Basin of Cornwall and Devon. To the north, as far as the Highland Boundary Fault, Middle Devonian sediments are missing, and a major unconformity separates Lower and Upper Devonian successions. A near-complete succession is preserved in the Orcadian Basin. The

Figure 9.2   (a) The distribution of Late Silurian to Devonian basins. (b) Representative stratigraphic logs for the main basins a–e.

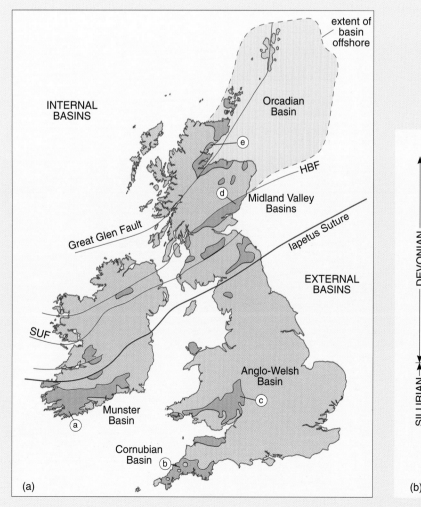

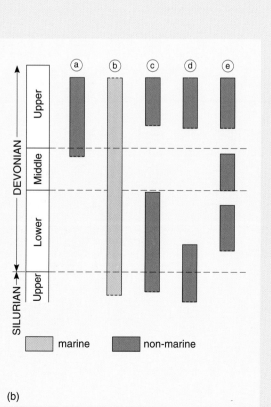

separate and distinct histories of different sedimentary basins indicate that individual basins were separated by topographic highs that acted as major drainage divides.

With the exception of the Cornubian Basin, the Late Silurian to Devonian basins preserve a record of non-marine sedimentation. The implications are that any residual marine Iapetan basins had been uplifted well above sea-level, and were either exposed and being eroded, or accumulating non-marine sequences. The mid-Devonian unconformity marks the period of maximum uplift and erosion. It was only in the south of the region, in the Cornubian Basin, that subsidence and deposition of marine sequences persisted.

9.4 Sedimentation and tectonics in the Midland Valley

9.4.1 Structure of the Midland Valley in the Devonian Period

The Midland Valley contained two Early Devonian basins, the Strathmore and Lanark Basins, which were separated by a central zone or axis of active volcanism (Figure 9.3). The Upper Silurian to Lower Devonian sediments laid down in these two basins are unconformably overlain by Upper Devonian sediments deposited in a larger basin, the Midland Valley Basin; Middle Devonian rocks are absent (Figure 9.2b). Outliers of Upper Silurian to Lower Devonian sediments and associated volcanics are found within the adjacent Grampian Highlands and Southern Uplands. The depositional age of the sedimentary rocks is constrained by the eruption ages of the contemporaneous basaltic, andesitic and dacitic volcanic rocks, radiometrically dated at *c*. 423–396 Ma (Figure 9.3).

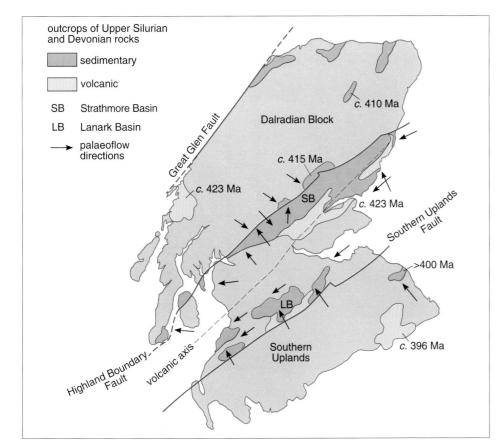

Figure 9.3 Map showing the distribution of Old Red Sandstone (Upper Silurian and Devonian) outcrops in the Midland Valley and adjacent areas. Arrows show the Lower Old Red Sandstone palaeoflow directions.

● What significant magmatic and tectonic events were happening at this time in this region? (Refer back to Section 8.)

● The Newer Granites were emplaced at *c.* 440–390 Ma, and important sinistral strike–slip displacements were occurring along NE–SW-oriented fault systems at *c.* 430–425 Ma and *c.* 410–390 Ma.

● What information in Figure 9.3 indicates that some fault displacements outlasted sedimentation?

● The Highland Boundary Fault truncates the margin of the Strathmore Basin and the adjacent outliers to the north; in addition, the Southern Uplands and Great Glen Faults also cut Devonian rocks. (These observations also suggest that the Early Devonian basins originally extended beyond their present outcrop.)

The outliers of sedimentary and volcanic rocks to the north of the Midland Valley sit directly on Dalradian sediments that attained some of the highest metamorphic grades during the Grampian event, as can be seen by comparing their positions in Figure 9.2a with the metamorphic map of Figure 5.12.

● What are the implications of these observations?

● The fact that the sediments and volcanics sit directly on the highest-grade rocks suggests that the deepest levels of the Grampian mountains had been exposed and the region was essentially eroded to a peneplain by at least *c.* 425 Ma.

This is not unlikely, because Ordovician and Silurian sediments from the Midland Valley and Southern Uplands have been shown to contain Dalradian metamorphic minerals, implying that the Grampian mountains had been supplying debris to the surrounding areas since *c.* 465 Ma (Section 6.4). Likewise, uplift and erosion of the Southern Uplands before deposition of the Old Red Sandstone is indicated by the unconformable bases of the Old Red Sandstone outliers.

In Late Silurian to Early Devonian times the Midland Valley and its neighbouring areas had the structure summarized in Figure 9.4. This provided the setting for the accumulation of the Old Red Sandstone in the Midland Valley.

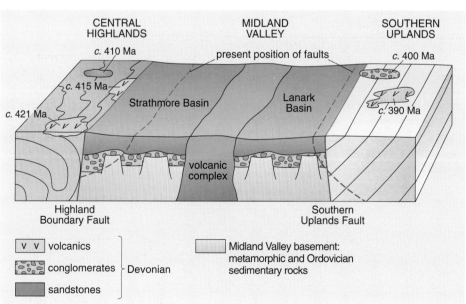

Figure 9.4   Schematic block diagram of the structure of the Midland Valley and adjacent regions in Late Silurian to Early Devonian times. The present positions of the major faults may reflect later compression of the Midland Valley.

9.4.2 Late Silurian–Early Devonian sedimentation

The early basin fill comprised conglomerates and breccias deposited in alluvial fans (Figure 9.5). The debris mainly consisted of reworked quartzites, granitic boulders, abundant andesitic volcanics, gabbros and dolerites. The gabbros and dolerites were probably sourced from remnant ophiolitic rocks that may underlie the Midland Valley. Detritus of Dalradian origin accounts for only a limited amount of these sediments. Palaeocurrent data (Figure 9.3) indicate that the sediments were sourced from several regions: from the NE and SW, from the adjacent blocks of the Grampian Highlands and Southern Uplands, and from the volcanic axis. It has been suggested that deposition occurred in a set of transtensional basins bounded by a series of active strike–slip faults (including the Highland Boundary and Southern Uplands Faults). The changing pattern of fault movements caused uplift in some areas and erosion in others, and led to the recycling of earlier deposits as areas of deposition became uplifted blocks. The early sediments were progressively recycled and reworked.

Figure 9.5   Near-vertical Lower Old Red Sandstone conglomerates in the northern limb of the Strathmore Syncline, Dunnottar Castle, south of Stonehaven.

By late Early Devonian times sedimentation in the basin had changed. The coarse conglomerates and breccias gave way to finer sands. Palaeocurrent data suggest a south-westerly flow along the axis of the basin, and indicate that the sediment was derived from the north-east. One possible explanation is that the sediments were sourced from the rising Scandian mountains and transported by major trunk rivers that flowed south-west along the axis of the basin. The fining-upwards of the sequence and the absence of significant Dalradian metamorphic debris suggest that the basin flanks or rift shoulders were no longer uplifting and providing debris to the basin.

9.4.3 A Mid-Devonian hiatus

Sedimentation in the Midland Valley ceased in Mid-Devonian times. Several lines of evidence point to a phase of convergence or transpression at this time. For example, the Early Devonian basins are folded on a regional scale, with NE–SW-striking fold axes. In addition, the Early Devonian basin-bounding faults may have been reactivated as thrusts, a process which led to truncation of the basin margins. The possible effect of the displacement on the positions of the major faults is illustrated in Figure 9.4.

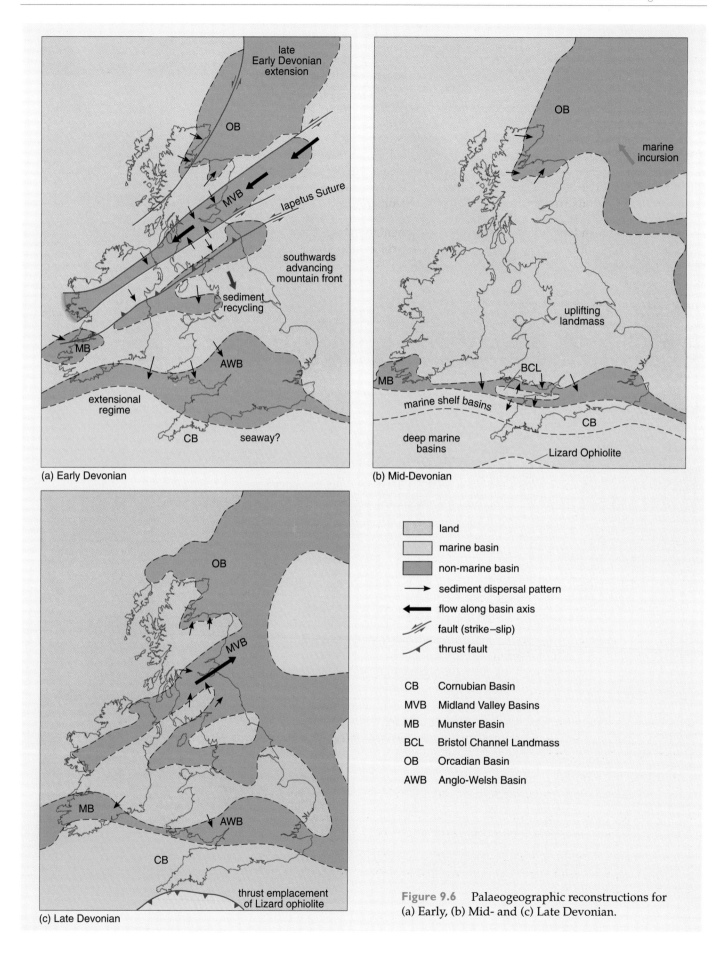

(a) Early Devonian

(b) Mid-Devonian

(c) Late Devonian

land

marine basin

non-marine basin

→ sediment dispersal pattern

➡ flow along basin axis

fault (strike–slip)

thrust fault

CB   Cornubian Basin

MVB   Midland Valley Basins

MB   Munster Basin

BCL   Bristol Channel Landmass

OB   Orcadian Basin

AWB   Anglo-Welsh Basin

Figure 9.6   Palaeogeographic reconstructions for (a) Early, (b) Mid- and (c) Late Devonian.

9.4.4 Renewed deposition in the Late Devonian

Sedimentation in the Midland Valley resumed in the Late Devonian. A series of northerly-derived alluvial fans, which deposited conglomerates fining upwards into muds, bordered an alluvial plain crossed by meandering rivers, from which essentially fine-grained sediments were deposited. Deposition was slow and allowed the development of calcareous cements and carbonate evaporites (caliches). Palaeocurrents indicate that the rivers flowed roughly NE, opposite to the Early Devonian drainage system, probably as a result of uplift in the SW. The changing pattern of sedimentation in the Midland Valley (and across the mountain belt) is illustrated in Figure 9.6, which shows a series of palaeogeographic reconstructions for Early to Late Devonian times.

In the eastern Southern Uplands, Late Devonian sedimentation deposited sandstones and conglomerates on upturned Silurian turbidites to produce the Siccar Point unconformity, famously recognized by James Hutton in 1788 (Figures 1.1 and 9.7).

Figure 9.7   The unconformity at Siccar Point, showing shallowly-dipping Upper Old Red Sandstone resting on steeply-dipping Llandovery turbidites.

9.4.5 Summary of Section 9.4

- Late Silurian to Early Devonian non-marine sedimentation in the Midland Valley occurred in a series of transtensional basins. It has been suggested that deposition was controlled by major strike–slip faults.

- By c. 425 Ma the mountains of the Grampian Highlands had been eroded down to their roots and the highest-grade metamorphic rocks were exposed.

- Initially, locally-derived detritus was supplied from the basin flanks. Later, externally-derived sediment was supplied by major SW-flowing trunk rivers.

- Mid-Devonian sediments are absent from the Midland Valley. Late Devonian sediments were deposited under conditions in which the regional drainage pattern flowed north-eastwards.

9.5 Sedimentation and tectonics in the external basins

9.5.1 A southward-migrating mountain front

Data from the external basins provide a picture of sedimentation and tectonics that is different from that obtained from the internal basins. In Late Silurian to Early Devonian times debris was shed southwards from the rising mountains and was deposited either in rapidly subsiding foreland basins or in fault-bounded extensional basins. It was only in the very south that the marine basins on the southern edge of Eastern Avalonia persisted. Figure 8.12 and Figure 9.6 show the overall tectonic and palaeogeographic contexts in which these basins developed.

Close to the Iapetus Suture, in the Lake District, Isle of Man and Ireland, Late Silurian deposition of debris occurred in rapidly subsiding foreland basins that developed as the Avalonian crust was depressed beneath the southwards-advancing load of Laurentia. In these basins, subsidence quickly gave way to uplift, shortening and erosion in the Early Devonian. As a result these early sediments were recycled and transported further south. A similar picture is observed in south-west Ireland (the Munster Basin) where gravels and coarse sandstones were deposited in a rapidly subsiding fault-controlled basin (Figure 9.6a).

In the Anglo-Welsh Basin, Upper Silurian marine sequences were replaced by non-marine deposits as sediment supply outweighed subsidence and basins rapidly filled. The composition of the Upper Silurian to Lower Devonian detritus suggests derivation from a metamorphic source, probably the Grampian and Northern Highlands. By Early Devonian times this source was waning and the majority of the deposits were derived from uplifting and eroding regions in northern England and North Wales, in essence recycling the earlier deposits. Deposition occurred in alluvial fans and flood-plains. Coarsening-upwards sequences indicate the southwards migration or advance of the mountain front.

By Early Devonian times, uplift and erosion was affecting all areas except Cornubia (Figure 9.6a). Maximum uplift was reached in mid-Devonian times and resulted in the widespread mid-Devonian unconformity. A periodically emergent landmass, the Bristol Channel Landmass, shed debris both north and south at this time (Figure 9.6b).

Alluvial and marginal marine deposition began again in Late Devonian times as a global sea-level rise caused the upwards transition into marine Lower Carboniferous sediments.

9.5.2 A short-lived mid-Devonian ocean basin?

In the south, the Cornubian Basin records the development of a small ocean basin. In the Early Devonian, fluvial sequences are thought to have covered most of Cornubia, the rivers flowing south into a marine basin (Figure 9.6a). In mid-Devonian times crustal extension led to the formation of a series of fault-bounded basins that developed on a marine shelf (Figure 9.6b). The most northerly of these basins periodically received sediments brought in from the north by rivers eroding the emergent Bristol Channel Landmass.

These southern basins had a history of fault-controlled sedimentation, indicated by debris flows, slumps and active volcanism sited along major fracture zones, with extension possibly continuing until the Early Carboniferous. Although the *c.* 400 Ma Lizard ophiolite may represent a fragment of oceanic crust, the basin was probably of limited extent and short-lived. By the mid-Devonian the basin was being filled by clastic sediment derived from the south, in response to the flexural subsidence ahead of the northward-migrating Variscan thrust pile. By the Late Devonian to Early Carboniferous, this small basin was being deformed by thrusting associated with the early stages of the Variscan Orogeny (Figure 9.6c).

9.5.3 Summary of Section 9.5

- By Early Devonian times, the Late Silurian marine basins had been uplifted above sea-level and non-marine sedimentation was occurring. As the Caledonian mountain front migrated south, early deposits were reworked by erosion and transported in river systems that drained into a marine basin. Sedimentation occurred in a series of fault-bounded basins that developed in response to the flexural loading of the crust.

- By mid-Devonian times, uplift and erosion had reached a maximum, as indicated by the absence of mid-Devonian deposits and the development of a major unconformity. In the south, continued extension-related rifting formed a mid-Devonian oceanic basin, which culminated in the development of oceanic crust.

- In Late Devonian times, the ocean basin closed by thrusting and renewed sedimentation resulting from pulsed marine transgression.

9.6 Orogen-scale drainage and sediment dispersal patterns

By Early Devonian times, the basement rocks of the Laurentian and Avalonian crust had been considerably shortened, the Lower Palaeozoic sedimentary successions had been folded, deformed and weakly metamorphosed, and the Silurian marine basins had been uplifted well above sea-level. As a result of the uplift a regional drainage pattern developed and rivers transported detritus away from the growing mountain belt. The palaeocontinental reconstructions shown in Figure 9.8 illustrate the changing pattern of the drainage system out of the orogen from Early to Late Devonian times. In the Early Devonian, an axial drainage pattern developed in response to uplift in the Scandinavian and Greenland segments of the orogen. This uplift generated a major drainage divide from which rivers shed sediment both NW and SW. These rivers transported sediment into the transtensional basins of the Midland Valley. Rivers originating in the Southern Uplands and northern England transported sediments towards the SE across the Iapetus Suture into the extensional fault-bounded external basins and into a marine basin, located along the southern margin of Avalonia. In mid- to Late Devonian times the drainage system changed as the centre of major uplift shifted south-westwards, and as a result rivers in the Midland Valley drained northwards and the mid-Devonian hiatus and regional unconformity developed across most of the region. Sedimentation only continued throughout the Devonian in the extensional fault-controlled Orcadian and Cornubian Basins.

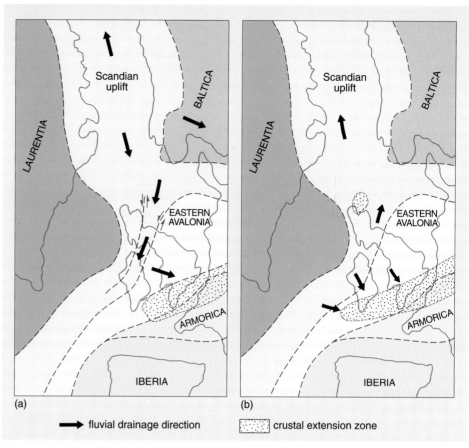

Figure 9.8   Late Caledonian orogen-scale drainage and sediment dispersal pattern for (a) Early Devonian, and (b) Late Devonian times.

9.7   Summary of Section 9

- In Early Devonian times, non-marine sedimentation occurred during convergence, with deposition of the Lower Old Red Sandstone within internal, transtensional basins, and external, fault-controlled rift basins.

- In mid-Devonian times, movement along strike–slip faults had ceased and uplift was at a climax. Uplift led to the development of a major mid-Devonian unconformity. At this time most of Britain and Ireland was shedding rather than receiving detritus. It was only in northern Scotland and along the southern margin of Avalonia that subsiding basins persisted. By Early Carboniferous times, marine transgression occurred and most of southern Britain came under the influence of the early stages of the Variscan Orogeny.

10 Legacy

Sections 2 to 9 summarized the origin of the crustal blocks, or terranes, of which Scotland is built and the plate tectonic collisions and strike-slip movements that brought those terranes together. Our geological saga ended some 350 million years ago, with the first ripples of the Carboniferous marine transgression and the distant rumblings of the Variscan Orogeny developing in Armorica to the south. Later events in Britain's geological history involved sedimentation during its northward drift across the globe, with bursts of igneous activity during the Carboniferous, Permian and Tertiary Periods, the last being associated with continental rifting and the opening of the Atlantic Ocean. In the main, however, the Scottish bedrock is made of rocks that formed before or during orogenic collisions between plates and micro-plates in the Ordovician and Silurian Periods.

The geology of the Highlands and its influence on the lives of people are therefore the legacy of Precambrian and Palaeozoic events. For example, hot springs of mineralized sea-water that were discharged from the faulted, stretched crust of the Laurentian continental margin during mid-Dalradian times deposited baryte, and this mineral is now mined from the enclosing metasediments in central Perthshire (at Foss) and used in the oil production industry. Shallow marine sedimentation during Dalradian (Southern Highland Group) times produced limestones, such as the Loch Tay Limestone, which 19th century farmers quarried and burnt to make fertiliser for the typically acidic Highland soils. Once crustal stretching and continental break-up had led to the creation of the wide Iapetus Ocean, plate convergence then brought Avalonia and Laurentia, and intervening island arcs, together. A series of terrane collisions ensued, with the collision of the Midland Valley Terrane and Laurentia deforming and metamorphosing the Dalradian in the Grampian phase of the Caledonian Orogeny. This c. 480–465 Ma mountain-building event also left many a mark. It was at this time that Dalradian metasediments melted during exhumation of the roots of the Grampian mountains to form granite, the defining building stone of Aberdeen (the 'Granite City'). The reason that Aberdeen is one of the places in Britain with a higher than normal level of background radiation is that the Ordovician Aberdeen granite inherited and concentrated radioactive isotopes from its source metasedimentary rocks. Silurian to Early Devonian subduction-related magmatism associated with the convergence of Avalonia and Baltica on Laurentia produced the granites of Lochnagar and the Cairngorm plateau, the andesitic volcanics of Britain's highest peak Ben Nevis and the igneous rocks of Glen Coe as illustrated on the front cover. During the final stages of orogenesis, the erosion of the high mountain range during the Silurian and Devonian, the Old Red Sandstone was deposited in the Midland Valley, later giving rise to the rich soil that supports one of the most productive fruit-growing areas in the UK.

Music, poetry, art and science have all been inspired by the rocks of the Scottish Highlands, and the introduction to this book (Section 1.1) mentioned some of the 19th century scientists whose geological work in the Highlands earned them places in the history of science. Perhaps it is no wonder that Charles Lyell, often considered to have founded the science of geology, was born and grew up in the shadow of the Highlands, some two kilometres south of the Highland Boundary Fault at Kinnordy, near the town of Kirriemuir. Present-day geologists still find much to puzzle about and enjoy in the rocks of the Highlands; the rocks themselves may be old but they continue to inspire new ideas and fresh insights on the way that mountains are built.

Acknowledgements

Every effort has been made to contact copyright holders. If any have been inadvertently overlooked, the publishers will be pleased to make the necessary arrangements at the first opportunity. Grateful acknowledgement is made to the following sources for permission to reproduce material within this Book:

Figures 1.2, 3.13, 8.5 R. A. Strachan, Oxford Brookes University; *Figure 1.4* R. E. Holdsworth, N. H. Woodcock and R. A. Strachan (2000) 'Geological framework of Britain and Ireland', in N. H. Woodcock and R. A. Strachan (eds) *Geological History of Britain and Ireland*, Blackwell Sciences Ltd; *Figure 1.5* adapted from T. H. Torsvik *et al.* (1993) 'Palaeogeographic significance of mid-Silurian palaeomagnetic results ...', *Geophysical Journal International*, **113**, 651–658, and T. H. Torsvik *et al.* (1996) 'Continental break-up and collision in the Neoproterozoic and Palaeozoic ...', *Earth Science Reviews*, **40**, 229–258, with permission from Elsevier Science; *Figure 1.6* B. J. Bluck, W. Gibbons and J. K. Ingham (1992) 'Terranes', in J. C. W. Cope, J. K. Ingham and P. F. Rawson (eds) *Atlas of Palaeogeography and Lithofacies*, The Geological Society; *Figure 2.1* adapted from R. A. Strachan (2000) in N. H. Woodcock and R. A. Strachan (eds) *Geological History of Britain and Ireland*, Blackwell Sciences Ltd; *Figures 2.2, 2.4, 2.5, 3.2, 3.5, 3.7* C. R. L. Friend, Oxford Brookes University; *Figure 2.6* adapted from B. W. D. Yardley (1989) *An Introduction to Metamorphic Petrology*, Longman Group UK Ltd, by permission of Pearson Education Ltd; *Figures 3.4, 3.6, 3.10, 3.12, 7.1, 7.2, 8.7–8.9, 8.12, 9.2, 9.6* adapted from N. H. Woodcock and R. A. Strachan (2000) *Geological History of Britain and Ireland*, Blackwell Sciences Ltd; *Figures 3.8, 3.14, 4.12, 5.18, 5.20, 5.21* K. A. Jones; *Figure 3.9* S. J. Daly, University College, Dublin; *Figure 3.11* K. A. Jones/C. R. L. Friend, Oxford Brookes University; *Figures 4.3, 4.8* R. A. Strachan *et al.* (2003) 'The Northern Highlands and Grampian Terranes', in N. H. Trewin (ed.) *The Geology of Scotland*, 4th edn, The Geological Society, London; *Figures 4.4b, 4.5, 4.10, 4.11a,b, 5.1–5.3, 5.5, 8.11* N. H. Woodcock and R. A. Strachan (eds) (2000) *Geological History of Britain and Ireland*, Blackwell Sciences Ltd; *Figures 4.6, 9.7* S. A. Drury, Open University; *Figure 5.4* D. McGarvie, Open University; *Figures 5.6, 9.1, 9.5* S. Blake, Open University; *Figures 5.7, 5.12* D. Stephenson and D. Gould (1995) *The Grampian Highlands*, 4th edn, HMSO for the British Geological Survey; *Figure 5.11* J. E. Treagus (1999) 'A structural reinterpretation of the Tummel Belt and a transpressional model for evolution of the Tay Nappe in the Central Highlands of Scotland', *Geological Magazine*, **136**, Cambridge University Press; *Figure 5.13* J. A. Winchester (1974) 'The regional metamorphic zones in the Scottish Caledonides', *Journal of the Geological Society*, **130**, No. 6, Geological Society, London; *Figure 5.24* T. J. Dempster, N. F. C. Hudson and G. Rogers (1995) 'Metamorphism and cooling of the NE Dalradian', *Journal of the Geological Society*, **152**; *Figure 8.10* from L. M. King (1994), 'Subsidence analysis of Eastern Avalonian sequences ...', *Journal of the Geophysical Society, London*, **148**, 207–210, with permission from the Geological Society, London.

Index